CW01023487

VIBRATION SOLUTIONS

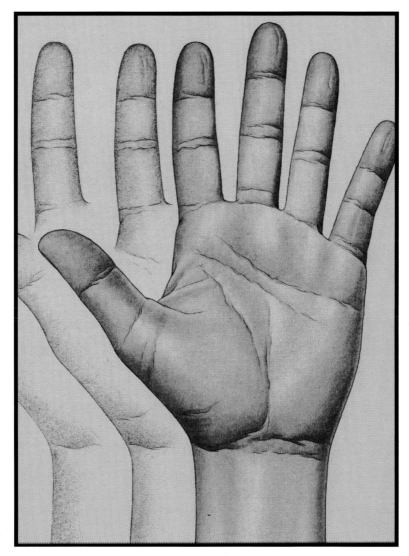

Practical ways to reduce the risk of hand-arm vibration injury

HSE BOOKS

This guidance is issued by the Health and Safety Executive. Following the guidance is not compulsory and you are free to take other action. But if you do follow the guidance you will normally be doing enough to comply with the law. Health and safety inspectors seek to secure compliance with the law and may refer to this guidance as illustrating good practice.

CONTENTS

Introduction.....1

How to approach a vibration problem.....3

Avoiding pitfalls when introducing vibration control.....7

Reduction in vibration exposure case studies.....10
Table of case studies sorted by vibration source...12

Case studies

1	Semi-automatic cut off machine...15
2	Off-line grinding wheel pre-forming...16
3	Introduction of low-vibration angle grinders...17
4	Crushing concrete...18
5	Water jetting...19
6	Bursting concrete instead of breaking...20
7	Diamond wire cutting...21
8	Pipeline insertion method avoids trenching...22
9	Directional drilling avoids trenching...23
10	Mounted roadbreaker...24
11	Reduced-vibration roadbreakers...25
12	Maintaining chainsaw anti-vibration rubber bushes...26
13	Chainsaw maintenance and training programme...27
14	Reduced-vibration chipping hammer...28
15	Sleeve for chipping hammer chisel...29
16	Isolated casting cut off...30
17	Automatic fettling of castings...31
18	Air-carbon arc gouging replaces traditional tools...32
19	Casting shell knockout in cabinet...33
20	Maintenance of low-vibration tools...34
21	Reduced-vibration needle guns...35
22	Shot blasting cabinet replaces rotary files...36
23	Descaling with abrasive blasters...37
24	Job rotation and use of pedestal mounted nutrunners...38
25	Automatic bolt fitting...39
26	Automated pallet stripping...40
27	Low-vibration power saw...41
28	Outdoor power tools purchasing policy...42
29	Low-vibration fastener system...43
30	No contact casting shell knockout...44
31	Low-vibration riveters and reaction bars...45
32	Special formwork avoids scabbling...46

33   Paint-on material avoids scabbling...*47*

34   Grit blasting instead of scabbling...*48*

35   Reduced-vibration pole scabbler...*49*

36   Deburring with rumbler...*50*

37   Belt grinding and polishing of metal fabrications...*51*

38   Group working with suspended tools...*52*

39   Installation of hydraulic cropping machine...*53*

40   Excavator reduces vibration exposure in quarry...*54*

41   Tool stock audit and purchasing policy...*55*

42   Hands-free linishing...*56*

43   Belt grinding and polishing of ceramic ware...*57*

44   Isolation for grinding operation...*58*

45   Laser cutter replaces nibbling machine...*59*

Maintaining blood circulation case studies.....60

46   Gloves to warm hands...*61*

47   Duct away exhaust air...*62*

48   Heated handles...*63*

49   Hot air to warm hands...*64*

Health surveillance.....65

50   Health surveillance on a construction site...*66*

51   Screening and surveillance methods in an aero-engine manufacturer...*67*

Table of case studies by industry.....69

Table of case studies by reduction method.....70

References.....71

Further reading.....72

Glossary.....73

Acknowledgements.....76

INTRODUCTION

Background

Vibration exposure from prolonged and regular work with powered hand-held tools, equipment or processes can have adverse effects on the hands and arms of users. Without effective controls, workers using such equipment may suffer various forms of damage, collectively known as 'hand-arm vibration syndrome' (HAVS). This is a painful condition and the effects can include impaired blood circulation, damage to the nerves and muscles, and loss of ability to grip properly. The best known form of damage is 'vibration white finger' (VWF), which is a prescribed industrial disease.

Legislation and HSE guidance

Under health and safety legislation[1,2,3] employers and machine makers must consider what action is necessary to reduce risks to health, so far as is reasonably practicable. HSE has published authoritative guidance, *Hand-arm vibration* (HS(G)88),[4] as a source of reference for those involved in identifying and controlling the risks of HAVS. It contains extra technical details to complement the case studies and includes sections on: hazard and control programmes; technical ways to reduce vibration; clinical effects and the health surveillance programme; and measuring hand-arm vibration. A list of other relevant publications is included in the 'Further reading' section.

Aim of the book

This book is aimed at managers and shows that vibration problems can be solved in many ways - but it is not exhaustive. It offers real examples of how some companies have reduced vibration at work. Although each industry has its own working practices, many vibration problems and solutions are not unique and are relevant in several industries. Vibration reduction should be considered at the process and product design stages, when selecting and purchasing tools, and when individual work tasks and work stations are being designed.

Check-list and advice for managers

This book includes a check-list for managers on approaching the problem of vibration and advice on avoiding pitfalls when introducing vibration controls.

The case studies

The case studies have been organised into three sections, each with a short introduction. These are:

(a) reduction of exposure to vibration;

(b) maintaining blood circulation; and

(c) health surveillance.

The tables at the beginning and end of the book provide an easy cross-reference to case studies for particular industries and to particular methods of vibration control.

Some employers have developed the solutions in-house. Other organisations have found that employing vibration consultants with wide experience in investigating hand-arm vibration exposure at work has led to effective, value-for-money solutions. To help employers, HSE has published guidance on employing health and safety consultants.[5]

Some of the language is technical and so a glossary is included at the end of the book. The case studies are designed to give managers an idea of what is achievable and are not meant to reproduce technical manuals.

Acknowledgements

HSE commissioned AV Technology Limited to gather information for the case study material in this book. We would like to thank them and the companies who agreed to be involved with this publication (listed on page 76).

HOW TO APPROACH A VIBRATION PROBLEM

Any worker who uses powered hand-held or hand-guided tools as a major part of their job may be at risk of developing vibration injury to their hands and arms. Many workers who need to hold workpieces in direct contact with machinery may face similar risks. In particular, any job that causes tingling or numbness in the fingers, or where finger blanching occurs, should be regarded as suspect. One course of action could be to measure the vibration, assess the exposure and take action in accordance with HS(G)88.[4] For powered hand tools, it may be easier to assume there is a problem when there is regular and prolonged use.

The check-list is designed to help you decide where problems might occur. It is followed by advice on vibration control techniques that might be used to get the vibration hazard under control. You may wish to discuss your conclusions with a vibration control engineer.

Find out where the main problems are

☐ Observe the work processes and the tools used. Where practicable and safe to do so, try the tool yourself.

☐ How many employees use powered hand-held tools and where do they work?

☐ Is there a high turnover of people in any departments using powered hand-held tools?

☐ Ask operators about vibration levels when the tool or machine is in use. Do they get numbness or tingling in their fingers?

☐ Have operators complained about recurrent pain or throbbing in their hands, or difficulties with gripping objects, or completing fiddly tasks such as fastening or unfastening a button?

Look at the process

☐ Could you redesign the process to avoid or reduce the use of powered hand-held tools, eg by substitution or mechanisation?

☐ Are alternative lower vibration processes or methods available?

☐ Could you introduce remote or power-assisted control?

☐ Could you use mechanical aids to help move the components or tools?

Look at the installation

☐ Could you reduce vibration from fixed machines by improving the mounting?

☐ Could you isolate the vibration directly?

☐ Could you use jigs to hold components firmly in place?

Look at the task

☐ Could you reduce or mechanise the force which the operator has to exert to do the job?

☐ Could you use balancers or tensioners to take the weight of the tool from the operator's hands?

Look at the tools

☐ Are you providing the most appropriate tools for the job? Check with suppliers whether lower vibration tools or components are available.

☐ Could you use an alternative type of tool, for example a grinder instead of a chipping hammer, to reduce vibration exposure?

☐ Could you buy better-balanced wheels or discs for cutting or grinding?

☐ Are you using the optimum quality and grade of cutting or grinding wheels and discs?

☐ Are the tools and machinery performing in accordance with the vibration values declared by the manufacturer?

☐ Could you reduce the airline pressure on hammer action tools and maintain cutting rates?

Check maintenance requirements

☐ Do your maintenance schedules conform to the manufacturer's specifications?

☐ Are your maintenance arrangements adequately supervised, monitored and recorded?

☐ Do you know how often tools or their components should be replaced? Do you need to replace anti-vibration mounts or dampers? Ask the manufacturer or supplier for information.

☐ Could you make balance checks on your tools and machines?

☐ Do you keep the tools sharp? Could vibration exposure from tool sharpening operations be reduced?

Look at the work schedule

☐ Could you reduce exposure by introducing job rotation?

☐ Are there enough breaks in the work for recovery during tasks with a risk of high vibration?

Check operator usage

☐ Are operators using the tools correctly in accordance with manufacturer's instructions?

☐ Do you train operators to use the correct tool for the job?

☐ Are the correct tools available?

☐ Should you introduce a 'permit to use' system for tools and processes with a high-vibration risk?

☐ Would closer supervision help?

Consider operator protection

☐ Do operators know what they can do to minimise vibration risks?

☐ Could you improve operators' information, instruction and training?

☐ Is the workplace warm enough to maintain good blood circulation, so preventing hands and fingers from becoming cold?

☐ Do operators need gloves or clothing to help keep them warm?

☐ Does the exhaust air from pneumatic tools need to be diverted away from the operator's hands?

Look at the costs and benefits

☐ Compare the costs and benefits of the various control measures. How many employees will benefit?

☐ Are there other benefits, eg reduced noise or improved productivity?

☐ What will be the cost per employee protected?

Look for symptoms

☐ Have you instituted a programme for identifying early adverse health effects?

☐ Do you have access to a medical practitioner to supervise the programme and for referral of symptoms?

☐ Do workers know what to look out for and are they encouraged to report symptoms such as finger blanching?

☐ Do you keep adequate records of these reports?

☐ Do you investigate any adverse health effects reported?

☐ Do you feed your findings back into your risk assessment and control measures?

AVOIDING PITFALLS WHEN INTRODUCING VIBRATION CONTROL

The following vibration control techniques are described in one or more of the case studies.

Process redesign

Ways of improving the process can often be found which not only reduce exposure to hazardous vibration but also improve productivity and quality. However, consider the following points:

☐ Ensure that when eliminating one hazard, eg by introducing a new technique or product such as changing from mechanical (buffing) to chemical polishing methods, you do not create a different hazard.

☐ Be aware that improvements in productivity resulting from process redesign could increase the vibration exposure of individual employees.

☐ Redesign may take time and require some investment. Other, possibly temporary, measures may be appropriate to introduce until the redesign has been completed, eg introducing job rotation.

☐ The product often determines the process. For example, the choice of decorative finish for building surfaces and the process used to achieve it can affect the exposure of construction workers to vibration. Can customer requirements be varied to minimise worker exposure to vibration?

Isolation

Isolation is the reduction of vibration passing from the vibrating machine, tool or component to the operator's hands. This can be achieved by the use of rubber bushes, sleeves and anti-vibration mounts. Consider the following points:

☐ This method is only likely to be practical in a limited number of cases and with expert advice. Each work situation should be assessed. Ask for specialist advice from the anti-vibration mount or material supplier.

☐ Incorrect application of this technique could increase vibration levels and may create additional physical hazards.

☐ If you apply it to new machines, you should check the manufacturer's guarantees to make sure that they will not be invalidated.

☐ Check that anti-vibration handles are suitable for the machine in question and will not affect the operation of the machine.

☐ Ensure that resilient sleeves are capable of reducing low-frequency vibration. Is the sleeve or wrapping thick enough? Get advice from the supplier or vibration expert.

☐ The resonant frequency of the anti-vibration mount must be well below the most important machine frequencies - usually the operating speed and related frequencies. Get advice from the supplier or vibration expert.

☐ Make sure that the mounts are not so soft that the tool or machine becomes uncontrollable.

☐ Make sure that a mount or anti-vibration handle failure cannot create a hazard. Get advice from a vibration expert.

Gloves

Gloves can play an important role in reducing the risks from hand-arm vibration. In cold conditions gloves will keep the hands warm, helping to maintain good circulation to the fingers. Gloves may also be necessary, or advisable, for physical protection of the hands. If you wish to supply gloves to your workers, you will need to ensure that they are appropriate for the tools and the task so that the wearer finds them comfortable and is able to manipulate the tools and controls properly without increasing grip or force.

Various gloves with special soft linings intended to provide vibration isolation are commercially available. These gloves can often reduce high-frequency vibration but have little effect at mid and low frequencies which are those most likely to damage blood flow in the hand. Anti-vibration gloves should be assumed not to reduce vibration exposure unless you have test data that shows otherwise for the combination of glove and tool used. Manufacturers continue to conduct research to develop better performing materials to reduce vibration at the hazardous frequencies.

New tools

Ask for vibration data for any tools that you are considering using or buying. Some helpful questions are suggested in Appendix 1 of HS(G)88,[4] and they are reproduced opposite.

Extract from HS(G)88 *Hand-arm vibration*

Purchasing new tools and equipment

When purchasing new tools and equipment, employers should ask suppliers for information on vibration. The following list suggests some possible questions.

1 Is the vibration of any handle or other surface to be held by the user likely to exceed an acceleration of 2.5 m/s^2, in normal use?

If the answer to question 1 is YES,

2 What is the frequency-weighted acceleration:

(a) under operating conditions producing the highest vibration?

(b) under typical operating conditions?

(c) under other standard conditions?

3 Under what operating conditions were the measurements made?

4 If the tests were in accordance with a published standard, provide details and indicate the extent to which the vibration may differ from the quoted values under normal conditions of use.

5 What measures have been taken to minimise vibration?

6 Are additional vibration reduction measures practicable? Give details of any design changes, the additional cost and any production penalties.

7 What is the maximum frequency-weighted acceleration that the tool or equipment can be guaranteed not to exceed?

8 What tests would be carried out to confirm any claims made in answer to question 7?

9 What other measures are required to minimise the vibration hazard to which employees are exposed when using the tool or equipment in question? Give details of any special maintenance requirements.

Do you know what the supplier's vibration data means? Remember that the data which the supplier has to provide is intended to help you choose the right machine for the job and your employees.

The vibration magnitudes quoted by manufacturers/machine-makers are intended to enable the potential purchaser to compare one maker's machines with machines of a similar type offered by another manufacturer. The vibration magnitudes of the machines when in normal use may be different. Ask the manufacturer for more information.

Ensure employees are aware that some low-vibration tools will feel different in use and may require a different operator technique to the traditional tools which they replace. Training and a period for employees to get used to using the new tools may be necessary.

REDUCTION IN VIBRATION EXPOSURE CASE STUDIES

These studies have been placed in order by vibration source. Each case study in this section describes the nature of the vibration problem, the solution applied by the company, the cost (at 1995 prices) and the vibration reduction and other benefits gained. Vibration reductions have been achieved by using tools or machines which produce less vibration, by reducing the amount of time spent using the tool or machine, or by introducing a new way of working which removes all exposure to vibration.

The vibration data for each case study is summarised in a table.

Understanding the vibration measurements and data tables

Vibration magnitude

Hand-transmitted vibration magnitude is measured in terms of the acceleration of the surface in contact with the hand. The acceleration of the surface is normally expressed in units of metres per second squared (m/s^2). Hazard to health is usually assessed from the average (root-mean-square or rms) acceleration level, using an instrument with a standard 'frequency weighting network' or filter to reduce its sensitivity at the high frequencies. This gives the 'frequency weighted acceleration' ($a_{h,w}$) in m/s^2, where 'h' indicates hand-transmitted vibration and 'w' indicates that the measurement has been frequency weighted. British Standard BS 6842:1987[6] describes a procedure for making these measurements.

The vibration magnitude figures quoted in the studies relate to specific tools in specific circumstances. Each situation should be measured separately. The figures may offer a guide only to the likely value when similar tools are used in similar processes (see HS(G)88[4]).

Daily vibration exposure

The vibration exposure, or 'dose', of a worker over a working day depends on the duration of exposure as well as the vibration magnitude at the gripped surface(s) of the tool(s) used. Exposure should be adjusted to a standard reference period of 8 hours (A(8)) to allow different exposure patterns to be compared and for the assessment of health risk. Programmes of preventative measures and health surveillance are recommended where workers' daily vibration exposure regularly exceeds 2.8 m/s^2 A(8).

Vibration data table

	A	B	C	D
	Vibration magnitude $a_{h,w}$ in m/s^2	Time before daily exposure exceeds 2.8 m/s^2 A(8)	Daily exposure time	Daily exposure (m/s^2 A(8))
Before	5	2.5 hours	3 hours	3
After	0	–	0	–

Example of table

The table gives the vibration magnitude ($a_{h,w}$) and details of daily exposure before and after action to reduce vibration exposure has been taken. In many cases the vibration is reduced to zero by the modification. The severity of the vibration hazard is indicated in column B which shows the permitted time before the daily exposure exceeds 2.8 m/s^2 A(8): the shorter the time indicated, the greater the vibration hazard. Action to reduce the risk may be required after only a few minutes daily exposure for some high-hazard tools. The relative risk of developing hand-arm vibration injury can be gauged by comparing either the actual daily vibration exposure time (column C) with the time before the daily exposure exceeds 2.8 m/s^2 (column B), or the actual daily vibration exposure (column D) with 2.8 m/s^2 A(8).

In some of the cases, for example Case Studies 11 and 40, the exposure values after the control measures have been applied remain in excess of the recommended HSE action level. In these cases, additional action should be taken to address the risks to health, for example, increasing the frequency or detail of health surveillance.

Explanation of 'before' and 'after' terms

'Before (estimated)' - this means that the data is based on estimates of the exposure that would have been caused by a process no longer in existence, or that the data has been provided to give an indication of the exposure that would have occurred if a high-vibration process had been used.

'Before (potential)' - this is based on the worst case hypothetical process that could have been used to do the work.

'Before (typical)' - this reflects the fact that the old technique could produce a wide range of exposures due to different vibration magnitudes and varying exposure times. The figures in the table give a good average for the type of work.

'After (potential)' - this is estimated data where the solution was not complete at the time of the research.

'After (typical)' - this is where the solution may lead to a range of vibration exposures due to variations in vibration magnitude and exposure time.

TABLE OF CASE STUDIES
(sorted by vibration source)

Case	Title	Vibration source	Industry	Exposure reduction technique
1	Semi-automatic cut off machine	Abrasive disc cutter	Investment foundry	Process automation
2	Off-line grinding wheel pre-forming	Grinding wheel dresser	Precision engineering	Process automation
3	Introduction of low-vibration angle grinders	Hand tool (angle grinder)	Shipbuilding	Tool design
4	Crushing concrete	Hand tool (breaker)	Construction	Change of machine
5	Water jetting	Hand tool (breaker)	Construction	Change of process
6	Bursting concrete instead of breaking	Hand tool (breaker)	Construction	Change of process
7	Diamond wire cutting	Hand tool (breaker)	Construction	Change of process
8	Pipeline insertion method avoids trenching	Hand tool (breaker)	Utilities	Change of machine
9	Directional drilling avoids trenching	Hand tool (breaker)	Utilities	Change of process
10	Mounted roadbreaker	Hand tool (breaker)	Utilities	Isolation
11	Reduced-vibration roadbreakers	Hand tool (breaker)	Utilities	Tool design
12	Maintaining chainsaw anti-vibration rubber bushes	Hand tool (chainsaw)	Forestry	Maintenance
13	Chainsaw maintenance and training programme	Hand tool (chainsaw)	Watercourse maintenance	Management
14	Reduced-vibration chipping hammer	Hand tool (chipping hammer)	Foundry	Tool design
15	Sleeve for chipping hammer chisel	Hand tool (chipping hammer)	Steel	Isolation
16	Isolated casting cut off	Hand tool (disc cutter)	Foundry	Isolation
17	Automatic fettling of castings	Hand tool (grinder)	Foundry	Process automation
18	Air-carbon arc gouging replaces traditional tools	Hand tool (grinder)	Power engineering	Change of process
19	Casting shell knockout in cabinet	Hand tool (hammer)	Investment foundry	Isolation
20	Maintenance of low-vibration tools	Hand tool (needle gun)	Construction	Maintenance
21	Reduced-vibration needle guns	Hand tool (needle gun)	Construction	Tool design
22	Shot blasting cabinet replaces rotary files	Hand tool (needle gun)	Shipbuilding	Change of process
23	Descaling with abrasive blasters	Hand tool (needle gun)	Shipbuilding	Change of process
24	Job rotation and use of pedestal-mounted nutrunners	Hand tool (nutrunner)	Automotive	Isolation

Case	Title	Vibration source	Industry	Exposure reduction technique
25	Automatic bolt fitting	Hand tool (nutrunner)	Automotive	Process automation
26	Automated pallet stripping	Hand tool (power saw)	Pallet repair	Process automation
27	Low-vibration power saw	Hand tool (power saw)	Pallet repair	Tool design
28	Outdoor power tools purchasing policy	Hand tools (outdoor)	Watercourse maintenance	Management
29	Low-vibration fastener system	Hand tool (riveting gun)	Aerospace	Change of process
30	No contact casting shell knockout	Hand tool (riveting gun)	Investment foundry	Isolation
31	Low-vibration riveters and reaction bars	Hand tool (riveter)	Aerospace	Tool design
32	Special formwork avoids scabbling	Hand tool (scabbler)	Construction	Change of process
33	Paint-on material avoids scabbling	Hand tool (scabbler)	Construction	Change of process
34	Grit blasting instead of scabbling	Hand tool (scabbler)	Construction	Change of process
35	Reduced-vibration pole scabbler	Hand tool (scabbler)	Construction	Tool design
36	Deburring with rumbler	Hand tool (straight grinder)	Turbine manufacture	Change of process
37	Belt grinding and polishing of metal fabrications	Hand tool (straight grinder)	Turbine manufacture	Change of tool
38	Group working with suspended tools	Hand tools (various)	Automotive	Management
39	Installation of hydraulic cropping machine	Hand tools (various)	Foundry	Change of process
40	Excavator reduces vibration exposure in quarry	Hand tools (various)	Quarrying	Change of process
41	Tool stock audit and purchasing policy	Hand tools (various)	Shipbuilding	Management
42	Hands-free linishing	Linishing machine	Investment foundry	Isolation
43	Belt grinding and polishing of ceramic ware	Pedestal grinder	Ceramics	Change of machine
44	Isolation for grinding operation	Pedestal grinder	Foundry	Isolation
45	Laser cutter replaces nibbling machine	Sheet metal	Turbine manufacture	Change of process

Note: Case Studies 46 to 51 do not have a vibration source.

SEMI-AUTOMATIC CUT OFF MACHINE

The task

Cutting multiple cast components from their runners and risers.

The problem

One of the traditional methods for cutting off cast components is to use an abrasive cutting disc mounted in a circular saw bench. In a typical day at one foundry the operator of such a machine could spend up to 3 hours exposed to vibration magnitudes of up to 5 m/s^2. The operation is also very noisy and there is potential risk of injury from contact with the exposed cutting disc.

The solution

Two fully-enclosed, semi-automatic cut-off machines were bought, principally to improve quality and efficiency. The multiple castings are clamped in rotating fixtures, trunnion mounted, and cut off with an abrasive disc.

The cost

The total project costs were approximately £70 000.

The result

- The operator does not need to touch any vibrating components.
- The operator controls the position and alignment of the castings and cutting discs at a distance.
- Manual handling of the components and exposure to noise, dust and sparks is reduced.
- The cycle time is cut.
- Less metal has to be ground off afterwards, which also saves time in the fettling shop.
- The risk of injury from contact with the cutting wheel is eliminated.

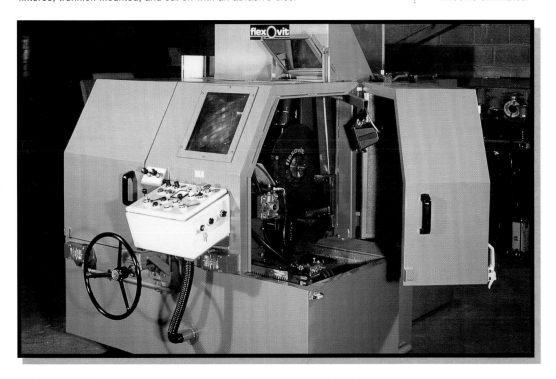

Automatic cut-off machines available from Flexovit (UK) Limited

Automatic cut-off machine

	Vibration magnitude $a_{h,w}$ in m/s^2	Time before daily exposure exceeds 2.8 m/s^2 A(8)	Daily exposure time	Daily exposure (m/s^2 A(8))
Before	5	2 hours 30 minutes	3 hours	3
After	0	–	0	–

OFF-LINE GRINDING WHEEL PRE-FORMING

The task

Dressing precision grinding wheels.

Diamond tool
(moving in the direction shown, guided by template)

Grinding wheel
(moving in the direction shown)

Opening cover

Template

Off-line grinding wheel dresser/pre-former

Case courtesy of Industrial Machine Tool Services Limited

The problem

Some companies have to grind components to precise shapes, dimensions and surface finishes. This is often done with grinding wheels that are profiled to give the required shape. During use, these wheels have to be frequently dressed to restore their correct shape and surface qualities. This is usually done with a dresser attachment mounted on a grinding machine, which either semi-automatically or fully-automatically profiles the surface with a diamond tool.

New grinding wheels are supplied in set widths, with no profiling. Cutting a complete new profile with the dresser attachment is very time consuming, so most companies pre-form their wheels before the dresser is used. The traditional method of pre-forming is to use a hand-held piece of carbide. This is extremely dangerous, both because of the risk of contact with the grinding wheel and because the operator is exposed to high vibration magnitudes. The actual vibration exposure varies depending on the size of the wheel and the piece of carbide in use. Operators reported severe wrist pain and numbness of the hands after just a few seconds of the work.

The solution

The wheels are pre-formed and dressed on an off-line dressing machine, which uses a mechanically driven diamond tool guided by a specially profiled steel fixture to cut the profile into the grinding wheel. The machine is fully automatic with a lid which must be closed before the cutting cycle can begin and cannot be opened until the cycle is complete.

The cost

An off-line dressing machine would cost about £12 000.

The result

- The operators are not exposed to vibration.
- There is little risk of contact with the grinding wheel.
- Productivity is increased by avoiding production machine down time.
- The operators' exposure to noise is also reduced.

	Vibration magnitude $a_{h,w}$ in m/s^2	Time before daily exposure exceeds 2.8 m/s^2 A(8)	Daily exposure time	Daily exposure (m/s^2 A(8))
Before (estimated)	40 (estimated)	2.4 minutes	5 minutes	4.1 (estimated)
After	0	–	0	–

INTRODUCTION OF LOW-VIBRATION ANGLE GRINDERS

The task

Weld dressing and fettling of metal fabrications.

The problem

At one shipyard the bulk of this work is done with 225 mm (9 in) electric high-frequency angle grinders. These are large heavy tools which often have to be held overhead or in awkward positions by the operator for an average of 1 to 3 hours a day. The company has just under 200 of these tools which produce average vibration magnitudes of 7 m/s^2, giving a potential exposure of over 4 m/s^2 A(8).

The solution

The company introduced a temporary solution to restrict the time for which 225 mm (9 in) grinders could be used, and to encourage the use of less powerful tools with lower vibration values for small jobs.

The long-term requirement was to use a grinder with both high performance and low vibration. In-house engineers reviewed all the grinders available on the market at the time and decided that a new design of pneumatic 225 mm (9 in) grinder featuring automatic correction for disc imbalance should be bought. Initial tests showed that these new tools using the company's usual grinding discs achieved a lower metal removal rate compared with the old electric grinders. Further testing revealed that by changing to a softer grade of disc, the pneumatic grinders could give a metal removal rate 40% higher than that achieved by the old tool/disc combination. The use of the new tools significantly increased the requirement for compressed air in the shipyard and it was necessary to upgrade the air distribution system to cope with the extra demand.

The cost

Self-balancing pneumatic 225 mm (9 in) angle grinders are approximately £700 each. The research and development took 1 month. The alterations to the air distribution system involved significant expenditure.

The result

- Vibration magnitudes are lower. In extended testing on real jobs in the yard, the new grinders produced an average vibration magnitude of 3.5 m/s^2.
- Efficiency is improved because of the higher rate of metal removal.
- The tools are much lighter and so they are easier and less tiring to operate.
- There are fewer risks associated with trailing electrical leads in the working area.

Reduced-vibration angle grinder

Equipment provided by Atlas Copco Tools Limited

	Vibration magnitude $a_{h,w}$ in m/s^2	Time before daily exposure exceeds 2.8 m/s^2 A(8)	Daily exposure time	Daily exposure (m/s^2 A(8))
Before	7	1 hour 17 minutes	3 hours	4.3
After	3.5	5 hours 7 minutes	3 hours	2.1

CRUSHING CONCRETE

The task

Demolishing concrete structures.

Concrete crusher demolishing a wall

Case courtesy of Specialist Services
(Cutting and Drilling) Limited

The problem

As part of the refurbishment of a hospital maternity block, it was necessary to demolish a 15 m long section of concrete wall. This could have been done with small pneumatic breakers which might have caused typical worker vibration exposures of 7 m/s^2 A(8) and created intrusive levels of noise.

The solution

The wall was cut away from the building pillars by drilling lines of overlapping holes (stitch drilling) using a diamond drill. The diamond drilling machine was held in a clamp and so the operators were not exposed to vibration. Each section was then broken up by 'biting' off pieces with a hydraulic concrete crusher. The jaws of this device close slowly, allowing the operators to loosen their grip before crushing takes place.

The cost

About 50% more than the cost of using pneumatic breakers on the same job.

The result

- The operator's exposure to vibration is negligible.
- Very low vibration is passed into the structure which helps to reduce damage and structure-borne noise.
- This method is less messy than using breakers as the debris is in larger pieces and less dust is produced.
- Noise levels are very low, both for the operators and the environment.

	Vibration magnitude $a_{h,w}$ in m/s^2	Time before daily exposure exceeds 2.8 m/s^2 A(8)	Daily exposure time	Daily exposure (m/s^2 A(8))
Before (typical)	12	26 minutes	3 hours	7
After	0	–	0	–

WATER JETTING

The task

Removing damaged or weathered concrete surfaces.

The problem

The deck and side walls of a reinforced concrete road bridge had decayed to the extent that surface repairs were needed. The top few centimetres of concrete needed to be removed and replaced with new material. The traditional method of removing the old material is to use hand-held pneumatic breakers, which can expose workers to typical vibration magnitudes of 12 m/s^2 for about 3 hours per day. The use of percussive tools can also damage the reinforcement bar, which then has to be repaired or replaced, and cause cracking in the base concrete which may weaken the structure. The operators work to a specified depth, often unnecessarily removing sound material and leaving areas of deep damaged material. The surface also requires thorough cleaning before new concrete can be applied. The job would have taken about 60 worker days with the breakers, as well as additional time to repair the reinforcement bar and other damage.

The solution

The job was done with a robot-mounted water jetting machine. This process uses an extremely high pressure water jet to wear away the old damaged concrete. The jet removes all concrete up to a certain strength, regardless of depth, leaving the good material and removing all of the damaged material.

The cost

A contractor using the water jetting machine took 15 days at approximately £1200 per day to complete the job (total cost £18 000). To do the job using hand-held breakers would have involved 60 worker days at approximately £150 per day (total cost £9000), plus the cost of repairs to the reinforcement bar and base concrete. These reinstatement costs often result in total project costs significantly higher than those for the water jetting method.

The result

- Operators are not exposed to any hand-arm vibration.
- The reinforcement bar was completely unaffected and there was no damage to the base concrete structure so it was immediately ready for the application of new concrete.
- The new concrete adheres better to the jetted surface.
- Airborne dust levels are very low as the debris is washed away by the water.

Robot machine water jetting a bridge side wall (left)

Concrete surface after water jetting (below)

	Vibration magnitude $a_{h,w}$ in m/s^2	Time before daily exposure exceeds 2.8 m/s^2 A(8)	Daily exposure time	Daily exposure (m/s^2 A(8))
Before (typical)	12	26 minutes	3 hours	7
After	0	–	0	–

6 BURSTING CONCRETE INSTEAD OF BREAKING

The task

Demolishing concrete structures.

The problem

During the renovation of a large warehouse, a temporary concrete retainer was built to support the external walls while the floors were removed and replaced. When the structural work was complete, the retainer, which was 1 m x 1 m in section and ran round the entire 300 m perimeter of the building, had to be removed. Traditionally this is done using small hand-held percussive breakers, as the vibrations from larger plant could damage the building structure. Such small tools have low material removal rates and expose operators to vibration magnitudes in the range of 5 to 20 m/s^2.

The solution

The main contractor hired a small specialist company to break up the retainer using hydraulic bursting. This involves forcing the concrete apart with a special hydraulic tool inserted into holes specially drilled for the purpose. Although the bursting process itself does not expose the operator to any vibration, in this case the holes were made with a rock drill which would have exposed the operator to vibration magnitudes as high as 15 m/s^2. The rock drill works fast, so the total daily exposure time was only about 10 minutes, which would give a potential vibration exposure of about 2 m/s^2 A(8). Vibration exposure could be eliminated altogether by using a clamp-mounted diamond core drill to make the holes. This would take slightly longer than the rock drill.

The cost

The rock drill and bursting method cost approximately 30% more than using breakers. The diamond drill and bursting method cost approximately twice that of using breakers.

The result

- The daily exposure time of the operators is reduced. This method is much quicker than equivalent low impact methods.
- Very low vibration magnitudes are transmitted to the building structure.
- Bursting produces very low noise levels and less dust and flying debris than pneumatic breakers.

Hydraulic bursting tool being used to demolish a retaining wall

	Vibration magnitude $a_{h,w}$ in m/s^2	Time before daily exposure exceeds 2.8 m/s^2 A(8)	Daily exposure time	Daily exposure (m/s^2 A(8))
Before (typical)	12	26 minutes	3 hours	7
After (actual)	15	17 minutes	10 minutes	2.2
After (potential)	0	-	0	-

DIAMOND WIRE CUTTING

The task

Removal of sections of brick or concrete structures.

The problem

As part of the refurbishment of a railway station, a new stairwell was to be cut through the top of a brick arched tunnel. Directly above the tunnel there was a solid floor, which was 1 m thick in the middle of the tunnel and 4 m thick at the sides. The aperture was to be cut through all of this material across the full 7 m width of the tunnel for a length of approximately 3 m. This job could have been done with hand-held pneumatic breakers. However, to avoid damage to the base structure, only low-powered units could have been used and the job would involve from 40 to 60 worker days of work. As tools of this type produce typical vibration magnitudes in the range 5 to 20 m/s^2 and may be used for long periods, vibration exposures of 7 m/s^2 A(8) or greater are possible.

The solution

The aperture was made with a large percussive breaker mounted on an excavator. Normally this would have led to severe damage to the remaining arch structure, but this was prevented by cutting right through the brickwork along the edges of the area to be removed. This isolated the delicate parts of the structure and allowed the material to be broken up in approximately 2 hours. The cuts were made in four sections with a diamond wire saw. This consisted of a diamond-toothed saw wire which was wrapped around the structure to be cut and driven by a track-mounted mechanism. As the wire cuts, it is pulled through the structure like a cheese cutter. For this job the wire was threaded through pilot holes drilled through to the tunnel from the floor above. This was done with a clamp-mounted diamond core drill.

The cost

£4500, compared with about £5000 for the same job using hand breakers.

The result

■ The operators are not exposed to any vibration from the cutting or drilling.

■ This method is much quicker, which means less disruption to the overall work programme. In this case, the total time on site was reduced to a total of 3 days, ie 1.5 days diamond drilling, 1 day diamond wire sawing and 2 hours breaking.

■ There is less noise and less damage to the structure.

Diamond wire cutter (NB The safety guards have been removed for the photograph)

Mounted breaker knocking a hole through a brick arch showing diamond-drilled pilot holes

Case courtesy of Specialist Services (Cutting and Drilling) Limited

	Vibration magnitude $a_{h,w}$ in m/s^2	Time before daily exposure exceeds 2.8 m/s^2 A(8)	Daily exposure time	Daily exposure (m/s^2 A(8))
Before (typical)	12	26 minutes	3 hours	7
After	0	–	0	–

The task

Replacing old cast-iron gas and water mains.

The problem

The traditional method of replacing old utility mains is to dig a trench down to the old pipe and lay a new one by its side (known as full-length trenching). This involves a lot of work both in digging the trench and in reinstatement afterwards. There is also a chance that other buried services might be damaged in the process. In urban areas it is also necessary to break road and pavement surfaces with percussive tools, which may result in high hand-arm vibration exposures.

The solution

It is now possible to replace old pipes without full-length trenching. One technique, which can be used in areas with compressible soil, involves splitting the old pipe underground and inserting a new one in the void. Two holes are dug about 3 m wide and 100 m apart to expose sections of the old pipe. A large pneumatic hammer fitted with a pipe splitting blade is then pulled from one hole to the other along the route of the old pipe with a powerful winch. The blade breaks up the pipe while the hammer body forces the fragments apart to make space for the new pipeline which is pulled along behind the pipe splitting blade. Additional small holes are dug down to reconnect branches to the new pipe and to remove old leak repair collars which the blade often cannot split. It took one utilities company approximately 2 hours to replace about 100 m of pipe.

The cost

About £10 000 for pneumatic equipment or £30 000 for hydraulic equipment. This equipment is also available for hire.

The result

- This method reduces the time the operators are exposed to vibration.
- It is much quicker than full trenching (about 25% of the time) and it reduces the chance of damaging other buried utilities or tree roots.
- There is less disruption to other road users and residents as there is less excavation and reinstatement.
- In areas with suitable soil it is possible to insert a pipe 25% larger than the old one which reduces the need for rider mains (ie extra pipes on the same route to cope with the additional volume).

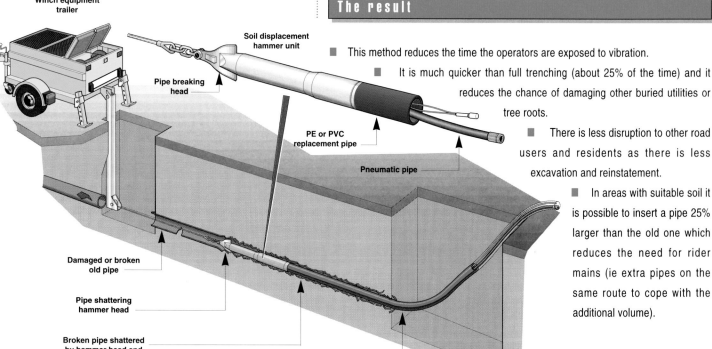

Winch equipment trailer

Soil displacement hammer unit

Pipe breaking head

PE or PVC replacement pipe

Pneumatic pipe

Damaged or broken old pipe

Pipe shattering hammer head

Broken pipe shattered by hammer head and pushed into surrounding soil

PE or PVC pipe pulled in behind hammer head

Pipeline replacement equipment

	vibration magnitude $a_{h,w}$ in m/s²	Time before daily exposure exceeds 2.8m/s² A(8)	Daily exposure time	Daily exposure (m/s² A(8))
Before (typical)	12	26 minutes	3 hours	7
After (potential)	12	26 minutes	30 minutes	3

DIRECTIONAL DRILLING AVOIDS TRENCHING

The task

Laying new utility mains.

The problem

The traditional method for laying utilities, eg water, gas and telephone lines, is to dig an open trench over the full length of the job and place the pipe in the trench in sections. The trenching operation causes considerable disruption and mess, and can be expensive. Road and pavement surfaces need to be broken up and reinstated using percussive tools. Workers are exposed to typical vibration magnitudes in the range 5 to 20 m/s^2 for an average of 3 hours per day.

The solution

Pipes for a new water main were laid without trenching across a motorway in northern England. The utility company hired a contractor who used directional drilling to lay the pipe. This technique, which can be used in areas with soft ground, involves digging a pit at each end of the pipe run and driving a steerable boring tool horizontally underground from one pit to the other. The head of the tool is steered from the surface using a mobile transmitter. After the boring is complete, the new pipe is pulled back through the hole. Small holes are dug from the surface down to the new pipe to connect the side branches to the main. There is a risk of disturbing other buried utilities, which can be avoided by following the HSE guidance book, HS(G)47, *Avoiding danger from underground services.*[7]

The cost

Equipment costs about £30 000. The total job costs about 75% of full trenching.

The result

- Vibration exposure time is reduced from an average 3 hours to 15 minutes per day.
- This method is much quicker (about 25% of time for full trenching).
- There is less reinstatement and less disruption to road users and residents.

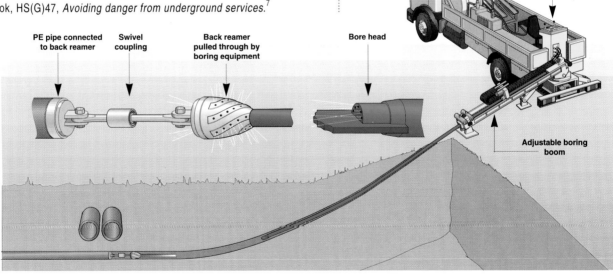

Directional drilling

	Vibration magnitude $a_{h,w}$ in m/s^2	Time before daily exposure exceeds 2.8 m/s^2 A(8)	Daily exposure time	Daily exposure (m/s^2 A(8))
Before (typical)	12	26 minutes	3 hours	7
After	12	26 minutes	15 minutes	2

The task

Breaking road surfaces

The problem

The most common tool used to break up road and pavement surfaces is the hand-held percussive breaker. These tools typically produce hand-arm vibration magnitudes of between 8 and 25 m/s^2 with an average of around 12 m/s^2. A full-time breaker operator working on a road excavation job might be exposed to this vibration for an average of 3 hours per day which would give a typical exposure of 7 m/s^2 A(8). The amount of work that an operator can do with one of these tools in a day varies depending on the depth and hardness of the surface to be broken up.

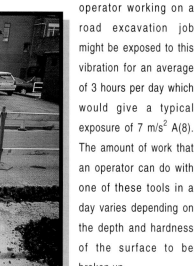

The solution

In some circumstances it is possible to greatly reduce the vibration exposure by using a larger breaker attachment mounted on the arm of an excavator. This method was used by a utilities contractor for digging telecommunications trenches in the road in a busy urban area. There was already an excavator on site for digging out the trenches once the surface had been broken, and the bucket was replaced with a breaker attachment, which took about 5 minutes, whenever required. The breaker is powered using the excavator hydraulics and is activated by a foot pedal. The arm position is controlled by a pair of levers, passing very little vibration (vibration magnitude is less than 1 m/s^2) to the operator's hands. A hand-held breaker, fitted with a sharp cutting tool, was used for about 5 minutes at the beginning of the day to score the edges of the area to be broken up with the mounted breaker.

The cost

Mounted breaker attachments start at around £3000.

The result

- This method reduces the time the operators are exposed to vibration. The exposure for the hand-held breaker operator was reduced to little more than 1 m/s^2 A(8).
- On the type of surface found in this example, the mounted breaker works approximately 10 times as fast as one person with a hand-held tool.
- The attachments on the excavator can be changed very quickly.
- Overall there is less disruption and noise.

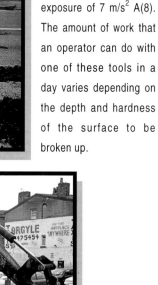

Mounted breaker being used to break roadway

	Vibration magnitude $a_{h,w}$ in m/s^2	Time before daily exposure exceeds 2.8 m/s^2 A(8)	Daily exposure time	Daily exposure (m/s^2 A(8))
Before (potential)	12	26 minutes	3 hours	7
After	12	26 minutes	5 minutes	1.2

REDUCED-VIBRATION ROADBREAKERS

Breaking concrete and asphalt road surfaces.

The problem

When installing or maintaining underground services it is often necessary to dig up roadways, pavements and other areas of hard standing, which usually involves breaking the surface with percussive pneumatic or hydraulic breakers. One utility contractor employed teams of workers to do this using a range of breakers of various types and ages. One tool, which was old but still in regular use, produced a vibration magnitude of 23 m/s^2 measured while breaking a road surface. On average, tools from the company's stocks produced vibration magnitudes of about 12 m/s^2. The workers had a variety of functions to perform so the actual exposure to vibration from breakers varied from day to day. Taking a typical exposure time of 3 hours, an exposure of over 7 m/s^2 A(8) could be experienced.

The solution

Many breaker manufacturers now make tools which they claim produce lower vibration magnitudes than older types with no loss of performance. These may feature redesigned mechanisms or some form of vibration isolation in the handle. The company bought or borrowed a selection of reduced-vibration tools from its regular suppliers and allowed a road gang on a real job to try them out and compare them. The vibration magnitudes produced by the tools were measured and the operators were asked to comment on their performance and ease of use.

One of the new tools, which featured softly sprung handles, produced the lowest measured vibration magnitude of 5 m/s^2. The operator felt that the soft springs made the tool difficult to control so that he had to hold the handles more tightly than the other tools, increasing fatigue. The next lowest vibration magnitude measured on another of the new tools with stiffer (rising rate) springs was 8 m/s^2. The operator found this tool comfortable to use and easier to control than all of the other tools on test. In future this tool will be bought by the company as they felt it offered a considerable reduction in vibration exposure over the existing tools while still having good performance and controllability.

The cost

Vibration-reduced breakers cost 25% more than the equivalent standard types.

The result

- The vibration magnitude is reduced.
- Tool operators are involved in choosing the preferred tool.
- Operators found the preferred breaker less tiring to use and it allowed greater precision than the others.

A selection of breakers

One of the preferred breakers in use

	Vibration magnitude $a_{h,w}$ in m/s^2	Time before daily exposure exceeds 2.8 m/s^2 A(8)	Daily exposure time	Daily exposure (m/s^2 A(8))
Traditional breaker design (typical)	12	26 minutes	3 hours (estimated)	7.3
New breaker design	8	1 hour	3 hours (estimated)	5

MAINTAINING CHAINSAW ANTI-VIBRATION RUBBER BUSHES

The task

Cutting wood with chainsaws.

The problem

Most modern chainsaws are fitted with rubber bushes which isolate the handles from the vibrating parts of the machines. Over time these bushes deteriorate through contact with oil and high temperatures. Generally they are replaced when they have split or failed completely. Their ability to protect the operator from harmful vibration will be reduced significantly well before complete failure occurs. One forestry company had a chainsaw that had been in infrequent use for approximately 3 years. The saw had been well maintained, with regular inspection and servicing and with the chain kept sharp and at the correct tension. The anti-vibration bushes were still intact but had become softened to the extent where they could be 'bottomed out' by pressure on the handles. In a normal wood sawing operation, a vibration magnitude of 9.7 m/s^2 was measured which would lead to a vibration dose of 2.8 m/s^2 A(8) being reached in about 40 minutes. The typical usage of such a tool might be 2 hours per day.

The solution

The bushes were replaced on a regular basis as part of a monitoring and maintenance programme.

The cost

Typical bushes cost about £5 each and can be replaced in about 1 hour.

The result

- The vibration magnitude, measured with the same operator cutting the same piece of wood as before, was reduced to 5.4 m/s^2. This would allow over 2 hours use in a day before reaching an exposure of 2.8 m/s^2 A(8).
- The operator had more control of the tool and found it more comfortable to operate.

Dismantled chainsaw with the five old anti-vibration bushes

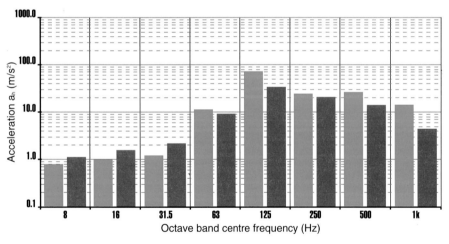

Frequency (Hz)	key	8	16	31.5	63	125	250	500	1k
a$_h$ with old bushes (m/s^2)	▪	0.8	1.0	1.3	11.0	72.4	24.9	26.2	14.3
a$_h$ with new bushes (m/s^2)	▪	1.2	1.6	2.1	9.3	34.1	21.3	14.1	4.4

Vibration acceleration measured on a chainsaw before and after anti-vibration bush replacement

	Vibration magnitude a$_{h,w}$ in m/s^2	Time before daily exposure exceeds 2.8 m/s^2 A(8)	Daily exposure time	Daily exposure (m/s^2 A(8))
Before (typical)	9.7	40 minutes	2 hours	4.8
After	5.4	2 hours	2 hours	2.7

The task

Use of chainsaws for cleaning river banks and watercourses.

The problem

River banks and watercourses are cleared using chainsaws and other power tools. One company introduced a tool purchasing policy designed to reduce the vibration exposure of staff to 2.8 m/s^2 A(8). This was done by buying chainsaws with a maximum vibration of 5.6 m/s^2, based on a typical daily exposure time of 2 hours (see also Case Study 28). The effectiveness of this policy depended on this vibration performance and work rate being achieved in the field, and it is possible that poor maintenance may lead to an increase in the vibration produced by chainsaws. For example, in a test it was shown that partially perished anti-vibration bushes increased the vibration magnitude produced by one saw from 5.6 m/s^2 to 9 m/s^2. In another test, a blunt chain cut at approximately a third of the speed of a sharp one fitted into the same saw, operated by the same person, cutting the same piece of wood. Since the workers have a fixed amount of work to do, it was possible that using blunt chains could triple the vibration exposure time.

The solution

The organisation approached the problem in two ways. Firstly, they developed a planned maintenance programme where every tool was serviced by a competent mechanic every 12 months. For each tool there is a service record sheet which has to be completed showing the condition of all major components including anti-vibration equipment. This should ensure that parts are replaced before they stop working and that tools are kept in good condition. Secondly, the tool operators themselves were given training in the correct maintenance of their tools (such as chain tensioning and regular saw sharpening), the risks of hand-arm vibration and the consequences of poor maintenance and blunt chains. This was done as part of the general chainsaw safety training the operators receive.

The cost

Tool servicing could cost approximately £50. Additional training costs were minimal as it was done as part of an existing training programme.

The result

- The vibration magnitude produced by the tools was reduced.
- Efficiency improved and there was a reduction in unexpected tool breakdown.

Chainsaw in use

	Vibration magnitude $a_{h,w}$ in m/s^2	Time before daily exposure exceeds 2.8 m/s^2 A(8)	Daily exposure time	Daily exposure (m/s^2 A(8))
Poorly maintained tools	9	46 minutes	6 hours	8
Correctly maintained tools	5.6	2 hours	2 hours	2.8

14 REDUCED-VIBRATION CHIPPING HAMMER

The task

Removing mould materials from the cores of large castings.

The problem

Many of the castings made in the foundry of a pump manufacturing company are hollow. They are cast around a sand core which has to be removed when the metal has cooled. This is done with a hand-held impulsive chipping hammer. The company had several old tools which typically produced vibration magnitudes of 8 m/s^2. Although the work was not done every day it was possible that on some occasions workers were exposed to vibration from these tools for up to 4 hours per day. This gave a potential vibration exposure of about 6 m/s^2 A(8). The extended periods of use were also quite physically tiring.

The solution

The work is now done with a vibration reduced chipping hammer which exposes the worker to a vibration magnitude of 3.7 m/s^2. The vibration has been reduced by the redesign of the internal components of the tool using springs and compressed air to isolate the tool body from the impacting parts.

The cost

The low-vibration chipping hammer used in this case cost about 25% more than the price of an equivalent normal one.

The result

- The vibration magnitude produced by the tool has halved.
- The new tool is much more comfortable to use for long periods.
- Tool performance is as good as equivalent high-vibration units.

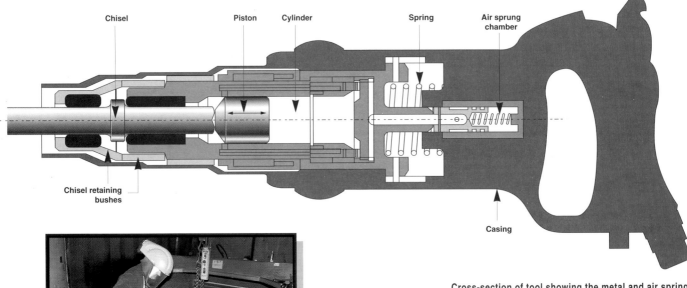

Cross-section of tool showing the metal and air springs used for vibration isolation

Low-vibration chipping hammer knocking out a casting

	Vibration magnitude $a_{h,w}$ in m/s^2	Time before daily exposure exceeds 2.8 m/s^2 A(8)	Daily exposure time	Daily exposure (m/s^2 A(8))
Before (potential)	8	59 minutes	4 hours	5.6
After (potential)	3.7	10 hours	4 hours	2.6

SLEEVE FOR CHIPPING HAMMER CHISEL

The task

Removing defects in steel castings using a chipping hammer.

The problem

At a large steel works, defects in steel castings are removed using pneumatic chisels or chipping hammers. Generally the toolpiece (chisel) is held in one hand while the trigger is operated by the other. Both hands are exposed to vibration but the chisel hand is exposed the most. On one tool a vibration magnitude of approximately 26 m/s^2 was measured. The exposure time for these tools cannot be predicted as it varies from day to day. However, the HSE recommended action level of 2.8 m/s^2 would be exceeded if the tool was used for about 5 minutes in one day.

The solution

Working together with a supplier of industrial rubber products, the steel company has developed a resilient sleeve to wrap around the chisel. This is most effective at reducing vibration along the line of the chisel.

Case courtesy of British Steel PLC, Swinden Technology Centre, Rotherham

The cost

Sleeves cost approximately £5 each.

The result

- The overall vibration magnitude has reduced to 13 m/s^2, half of its original value.
- The sleeve provides thermal insulation between the chisel and the operator's hand and is more comfortable for the operator.

Note: In addition to the development of the chisel sleeve, the company has introduced reduced-vibration grinders which are able to remove most defects.

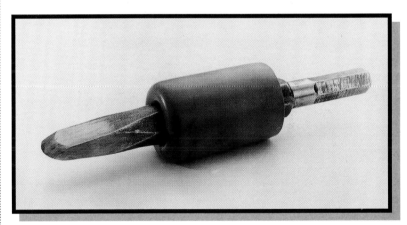

Chisel fitted with resilient sleeve

	Vibration magnitude $a_{h,w}$ in m/s^2	Time before daily exposure exceeds 2.8 m/s^2 A(8)	Daily exposure time	Daily exposure (m/s^2 A(8))
Before	26	5 minutes	Varies	Varies
After	13	20 minutes	Varies	Varies

ISOLATED CASTING CUT OFF

The task

Cutting runners and risers from cast components.

The problem

In a small alloy steel foundry, runners and risers used to be cut from castings using 225 mm (9 in) hand-held disc cutters. Over a typical working cycle, this operation produced an average vibration magnitude of 5 m/s^2. Operators could have been exposed to this vibration for up to 5 hours a day, giving a potential vibration exposure of 4 m/s^2 A(8). The eight workers in the fettling area used 25 000 cutting discs per year. The work also resulted in high noise exposure and a lot of manual handling.

Cutting off a casting with a hand-held tool

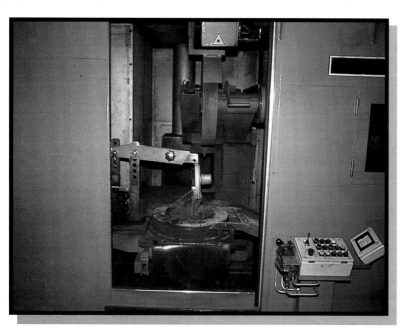

The solution

As part of a general programme to improve ergonomics and reduce vibration exposure in the fettling area, the company bought an enclosed remote-controlled cut-off machine. The casting is mounted in a simple fixture and cut by a large abrasive disc on a hydraulic arm. The operator watches the cutting through a window in the enclosure and does not come into contact with any vibrating components.

The cost

£135 000 for the cut-off machine. Disc costs have reduced by approximately 80%. The machine paid for itself in 4 years both through improved productivity and greatly reduced disc consumption.

The result

■ The operators are not exposed to any vibration.

■ It has helped in the programme to reduce back injuries at the foundry.

■ The exposure to noise, dust and fumes has reduced.

■ The risk of injury by contact with the cutter or hot metal is reduced.

■ More work can be processed by the same number of workers.

Automatic cut-off machine showing a casting in a fixture

Case courtesy of Terrill Bros. (Founders) Limited

	Vibration magnitude $a_{h,w}$ in m/s^2	Time before daily exposure exceeds 2.8 m/s^2 A(8)	Daily exposure time	Daily exposure (m/s^2 A(8))
Before	5.5	2 hours	5 hours	4
After	0	–	0	–

AUTOMATIC FETTLING OF CASTINGS

The task

Fettling spheroidal carbon steel castings.

The problem

The company operates a foundry that casts components in spheroidal carbon steels. These materials are very hard and, as a result, fettling (the removal of excess material after casting) has to be done with high-performance tools. People working in the fettling area can be exposed to grinder vibration for up to 3.5 hours a day. The large high-frequency electric grinders used at the factory can produce typical vibration magnitudes of around 7 m/s^2, so it is possible that people doing this work received a vibration exposure of about 5 m/s^2 A(8).

The solution

Much of the fettling is now done with a fully-automated robot-based machine. The castings are mounted on special fixtures and placed onto a conveyor system. A robot arm then picks up the fixture and manipulates the casting so that the unwanted material is removed by large grinding and cut-off wheels. The control sequences are pre-programmed, so all the operator has to do is mount the castings onto the fixtures.

Case courtesy of Triplex Williams Limited

The cost

About £250 000 for each automatic fettling machine.

The result

- The operators are not exposed to any vibration.
- There is improved productivity and more consistent quality.
- There is reduced exposure to noise, dust and fumes.

Inside the fettling machine, showing a casting mounted in a fixture and the grinding wheel

	Vibration magnitude a$_{h,w}$ in m/s^2	Time before daily exposure exceeds 2.8 m/s^2 A(8)	Daily exposure time	Daily exposure (m/s^2 A(8))
Before	7	1 hour 17 minutes	3.5	4.6
After	0	–	0	–

AIR-CARBON ARC GOUGING REPLACES TRADITIONAL TOOLS

The task

Rectifying defects in large castings.

The problem

An engineering company needed to refurbish two steam chests, which are large specialist steel castings weighing about 20 tonnes each. They had both been in service for some years and had many defects from use and previous repairs. Non-destructive testing techniques were used to detect and locate the defects, which included cracks and holes in the surface, hidden voids, and areas where an incorrect material had been added. To repair the defects, approximately 2 tonnes of material needed to be removed from each casting by gouging. Traditional tools, such as chipping hammers and grinders, would have taken a team of workers several months to complete and they would have been exposed to a high vibration magnitude.

Steam chest casting showing large area removed by thermal gouging

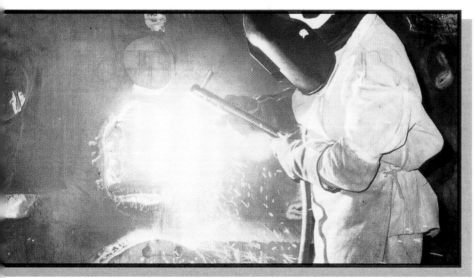

Air-carbon arc gouging in process

Case courtesy of Mitsui Babcock Energy Services Ltd

The solution

The company removed the material using air-carbon arc gouging. This process uses an arc welding power source and a special hand set with a nozzle that blasts compressed air onto the arc, blowing away the molten metal.

The cost

Air-carbon arc gouging equipment costs approximately £7000 per set.

The result

- The operators were not exposed to any vibration.
- This method gave a higher material removal rate than chipping and grinding, which led to large savings in time and cost. For example, the job was completed by four men in about 1 month.

Note: The process produced copious volumes of airborne fume and spatter. Operators must be protected and other people removed from the area. Failure to do so will put the health of operators at serious risk. Companies should perform a detailed assessment of the risks to the health and safety of operators and ensure fume levels are controlled to the appropriate level. This may result in additional costs. It may also produce high noise levels from which operators must be protected.

There are various other methods of thermal gouging which are suitable for different applications and many have lower exposure to these other hazards. The two main alternatives are oxy-fuel gas flame gouging and plasma gouging.

	Operation	Vibration magnitude $a_{h,w}$ in m/s^2	Time before daily exposure exceeds 2.8 m/s^2 A(8)	Daily exposure time	Daily exposure (m/s^2 A(8))
Before (potential)	Grinding	9	46 minutes	3 hours	5.5
	Chipping	13	22 minutes	3 hours	8
After	–	0	–	0	–

CASTING SHELL KNOCKOUT IN CABINET

The task

Removing ceramic mould shells from precision cast components.

The problem

At one small foundry, ceramic mould shells used to be removed by hand using a lump hammer. This was very time consuming and not particularly effective at removing all of the mould material. Hand hammering operations like this expose workers to high magnitudes of shock vibration - over a typical working cycle, values as high as 27 m/s^2 are common. Each mould shell took about 2 minutes to knock out. The number done per day varied and the work was shared between two or three people. If one person knocked out ten moulds in a day their vibration exposure would have been about 6 m/s^2 A(8).

The solution

The company bought a knockout cabinet. This consists of a chipping hammer mounted in a steel frame inside an acoustically treated enclosure. The casting is placed in the cabinet and the chipper will only operate when the door is closed.

The cost

£5000 to purchase and fit out the cabinet.

The result

- The operator is not exposed to vibration.
- There is a small reduction in manual handling.
- It is a much faster method (eight times faster than the old method) and more effective.
- Noise exposures are lower than alternative methods.
- There is less mess around the workshop as the removed ceramic is all in one place, reducing clean up time.

Casting inside cabinet before operation begins

Automatic knockout cabinet and operator

Casting inside cabinet after mould removal

	Vibration magnitude $a_{h,w}$ in m/s^2	Time before daily exposure exceeds 2.8 m/s^2 A(8)	Daily exposure time	Daily exposure (m/s^2 A(8))
Before (typical)	27	5 minutes	20 minutes	5.5
After	0	–	0	0

MAINTENANCE OF LOW-VIBRATION TOOLS

The task

Using a needle gun.

The problem

As part of a programme to reduce hand-arm vibration exposure, one construction company tried out a new vibration-reduced needle gun. The manufacturer claimed a vibration magnitude of 4 m/s^2 (tested to the relevant laboratory standard). This was considered acceptable by the company as the tools would not be used for more than 4 hours per day and the operators would not be exposed to vibration from other sources. The tool was used on a large site for a few months without any regular maintenance. During a check on vibration levels performed on-site, the needle gun produced a vibration magnitude of 15 m/s^2. The company returned the tool to the manufacturers for repairs and comment.

The solution

The tool was dismantled and it was discovered that only six of the original 28 needles were still intact and that part of one of the broken needles was jamming the vibration isolation system. There was no damage to the other internal components of the tool which had still been usable even in its damaged state. The needles and needle guide were replaced, the tool was reassembled and tested for vibration again. Under similar load conditions to before, a magnitude of 4 m/s^2 was measured. The vibration exposure caused by the poorly-maintained tool will be avoided in future by more rigorous monitoring of the tool's condition.

The cost

Basic maintenance can be done in-house. The cost of a manufacturer's service will depend on the type of tool.

The result

- The vibration magnitude is reduced.
- Properly maintained tools tend to last longer and retain performance and productivity

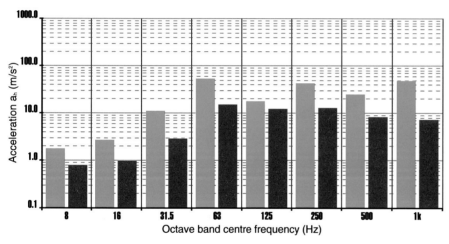

Frequency (Hz)	key	8	16	31.5	63	125	250	500	1k
a$_h$ for damaged gun (m/s^2)	■	1.8	2.8	10.2	53.3	17.8	42.0	22.5	44.7
a$_h$ for repaired gun (m/s^2)	■	0.8	1.0	3.2	15.3	11.7	12.3	8.6	6.5

Vibration acceleration measured on a needle gun before and after it was repaired

The repaired needle gun

	Vibration magnitude a$_{h,w}$ in m/s^2	Time before daily exposure exceeds 2.8 m/s^2 A(8)	Daily exposure time	Daily exposure (m/s^2 A(8))
Before	15	19 minutes	4	10.6
After	4	4 hours	4	2.8

REDUCED-VIBRATION NEEDLE GUNS

The task

Large-scale concrete construction.

The problem

The building of large concrete structures often involves scabbling. This involves roughing up concrete with percussive tools to form a bonding surface which will make a good joint where additional concrete is to be added. This can be done with a variety of tools depending on access requirements. On one site, hand-held needle guns were used to scabble a range of surfaces. Some of these tools were tested at the site and produced vibration magnitudes of between 9 and 13 m/s^2 while scabbling. As the tools may be used for up to 2 hours in a typical day, this would give a maximum vibration exposure of 6.5 m/s^2 A(8).

The solution

There are several methods which could reduce vibration exposure due to scabbling. One involves the use of new low-vibration needle guns which were used as direct replacements for the old tools. On one of the new tools, a vibration magnitude of 4 m/s^2 was measured while scabbling concrete, which was a significant improvement over the older tools on the site. The internal design of the tool uses springs, rubber and compressed air to isolate the vibration from the operator.

The cost

The tool in this case costs about 10% more than the price of an equivalent normal tool.

The result

■ The vibration magnitude has reduced.
■ Operators report that the tool is more pleasant to use.

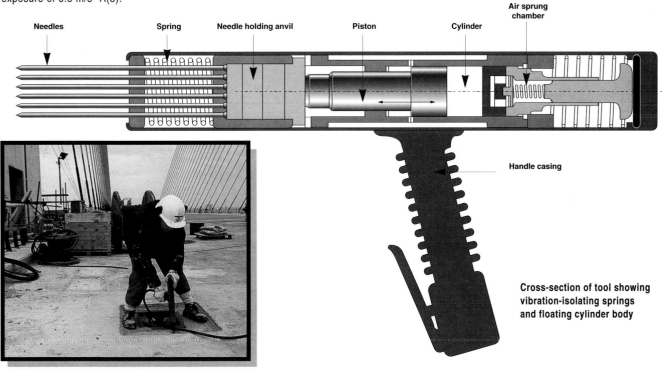

Cross-section of tool showing vibration-isolating springs and floating cylinder body

Vibration-reduced needle gun

	Vibration magnitude $a_{h,w}$ in m/s^2	Time before daily exposure exceeds 2.8 m/s^2 A(8)	Daily exposure time	Daily exposure (m/s^2 A(8))
Before (potential)	13	22 minutes	2 hours	6.5
After (potential)	4	4 hours	2 hours	2

SHOT BLASTING CABINET REPLACES ROTARY FILES

The task

Descaling very large castings.

The problem

Submarine buoyancy tanks contain large intricately shaped vents called grillages through which water and air are pumped in and out. These grillages are generally made of cast metal and require fettling and descaling before they can be fitted to the ship. Because of their complex shape, at one shipbuilding company this job was done by a team of 30 people with rotary files. They would work all day for several weeks on each grillage and could be exposed to vibration magnitudes over 5 m/s^2. Noise and dust levels were also extremely high.

The solution

The company already had a very large shot blasting cabinet which was used for surface preparation of other items. This cabinet was adapted so that the grillages could pass through on a conveyor system. A machine uses compressed air to blast small metal balls (shot) at the surfaces of the grillage. This 'shot-blasting' dislodges and removes the scale. One operator is required, who stands away from the noise and dust, and is not exposed to any hand-arm vibration.

The cost

Approximately £50 000.

The result

- The operator is not exposed to vibration.
- There is reduced exposure to noise and dust.
- What used to take a team 3 weeks can now be done by one person in 1 day.

	Vibration magnitude $a_{h,w}$ in m/s^2	Time before daily exposure exceeds 2.8 m/s^2 A(8)	Daily exposure time	Daily exposure (m/s^2 A(8))
Before	5	2 hours 30 minutes	6 hours	4.3
After	0	–	0	–

DESCALING WITH ABRASIVE BLASTERS

The task

Cleaning the insides of large storage tanks to remove rust, scale and other impurities after fabrication.

The problem

A large shipbuilding company used to clean out tanks using needle scalers. This operation exposed staff to vibration magnitudes in the range 11 to 23 m/s^2 often for more than 7 hours a day. Conditions inside the tank were also extremely unpleasant with high noise levels and clouds of dust.

The solution

The needle scalers were replaced with portable vacuum blasting machines which clean the surfaces by blasting them with an abrasive material and then sucking it and any debris away to a holding tank. The operator is exposed to vibration magnitudes below 1 m/s^2.

**Educt-o-matic machine available from
Hodge-Clemco Limited**

The cost

About £1000 for the vacuum blasting machine.

The result

- A reduction in vibration magnitude from up to 23 m/s^2 to less than 1 m/s^2.
- A large reduction in both noise and dust levels. The vacuum action of the equipment removes dust and debris which previously made the work environment very unpleasant.
- A smaller team of operators is required to clean the tanks which has led to improved productivity and cost savings.

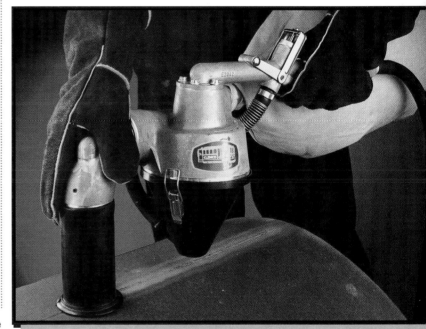

Vacuum blasting machine

	Vibration magnitude $a_{h,w}$ in m/s^2	Time before daily exposure exceeds 2.8 m/s^2 A(8)	Daily exposure time	Daily exposure (m/s^2 A(8))
Before	23	7 minutes	7 hours	21
After	1	More than 24 hours	7 hours	1

The task

Tightening threaded fastenings and attachments.

The problem

On one engine assembly line, a temporary adapter is necessary for feeding oil to the engine sump during on-line tests. It is screwed into a threaded hole on the side of the engine block. It does not need to be tightened to a specific torque but needs to be quite tight. This used to be done with a hand-held pneumatic ratchet gun of the type used in garages to tighten wheel nuts, which could produce vibration magnitudes up to 8 m/s^2. A maximum of 2400 engines are assembled per day, which, with perhaps 3 seconds ratcheting on each, would give an exposure of 4 m/s^2 A(8). The work was done by a group of about five people.

The solution

The company implemented a job rotation scheme whereby operators moved between four or five different tasks all around the same area of the production line. Some of the other activities involve some vibration exposure, but in general the rotation has halved individual exposure time. To further reduce exposure, the company opted to use pedestal-mounted nutrunners instead of ratchet guns to do the job. These are very solidly mounted and so pass very little vibration to the operator.

The cost

About £5000 for the pedestal mounting and tool.

The result

- Vibration magnitude is reduced.
- Less noise is produced by the pedestal-mounted tool than the ratchet gun.
- Operators report that the group working reduces boredom and fatigue.

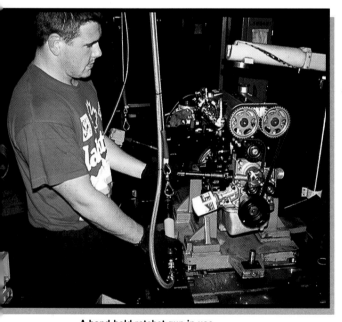

A hand-held ratchet gun in use

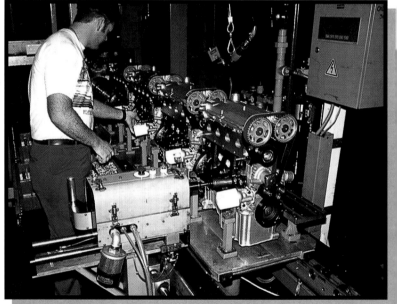

A pedestal-mounted nutrunner

Case courtesy of Ford Motor Company

	Vibration magnitude $a_{h,w}$ in m/s^2	Time before daily exposure exceeds 2.8 m/s^2 A(8)	Daily exposure time	Daily exposure (m/s^2 A(8))
Before	8	1 hour	2 hours	4
After	Less than 1	More than 24 hours	1 hour	Less than 1

AUTOMATIC BOLT FITTING

The task

Fitting main bearing caps to car engines.

The problem

The company used to fit main bearings to engine blocks manually. Using this method, the retaining bolts are started by hand and then run-up and tightened up, or 'torqued', using hand-held pneumatic or electric tools. These tools often produced high vibration magnitudes up to 8 m/s^2 and were in almost constant use as engines passed on the production line. It took two people to fit the bearing caps quickly enough to keep up with the other parts of the line.

The solution

In one plant the process has been automated. The bearing caps are placed in a fixture by robot arms and fitted by a dedicated machine which picks and places all five caps.

The cost

Ten spindle auto nutrunners cost £100 000.

The result

- The operators are not exposed to any vibration.
- The noise exposure of operators has reduced.
- Consistency and productivity has improved. For example, what was done by two full-time people can now be done by one, who also has hands free for other tasks.

The machine in operation showing a row of five bearing caps about to be lifted onto a cylinder head and fastened down

Multiple tightening spindles of the type used to simultaneously tighten the ten bearing cap bolts

Case courtesy of Ford Motor Company

	Vibration magnitude $a_{h,w}$ in m/s^2	Time before daily exposure exceeds 2.8 m/s^2 A(8)	Daily exposure time	Daily exposure (m/s^2 A(8))
Before (potential)	8	1 hour	6 hours	7
After	0	–	0	–

The task

Repairing wooden pallets.

The problem

The company own and lease out pallets. When the pallets are damaged they are repaired in special depots around the country. On arrival at the depot, the pallets are sorted and their defects identified. Damaged parts are then removed by prising apart the joints and cutting through the nails with a pneumatic saw. The saws used have a reciprocating action and are used in short bursts for a total of about 1 hour per day. The company wanted to reduce the resulting hand-arm vibration exposure by as much as possible.

The most time-consuming pallet elements to remove are the stringers. These are the strong pieces which run across the pallet to support the top planks and are held in place with more nails than the other parts. The stringer nails are also more difficult to access, which results in a lot of manual handling.

The solution BRISTOL DEPOT

As part of an overall programme to reduce a range of hazards and improve efficiency, approved by an ergonomist, the company decided to automate the stringer stripping process. They introduced specially constructed stringer stripping machines where the pallets are clamped to a bench and a circular blade is forced through the nails. Workers in the plant rotate jobs, so some vibration exposure is still experienced due to the use of the saws on the non-stringer parts.

The cost

No costs available.

The result

- The stringer strippers do not expose their operators to any vibration and they greatly reduce the amount of manual handling.
- The time the operators are exposed to vibration during the day has reduced.
- Overall the introduction of the stringer strippers has reduced the vibration exposure of workers by 13% and reduced the occurrence of upper limb and back injuries.

> Two depots in the company - Bristol and Birmingham - introduced different solutions to the problem.

Case courtesy of Chep (UK) Limited
Bristol depot

Hand-held nail saw used to dismantle a pallet

Stringer stripping machine

LOW-VIBRATION POWER SAW

At one of its sites the company has taken advantage of advances in tool design and bought new saws of similar performance which produce much lower vibration magnitudes. The new saws have been carefully designed to have a more balanced and smooth operation than the older types.

The cost

A new low-vibration saw costs about 11% more than the old type.

Summary - the combined effect

In the future, the company intends to introduce the benefits of both solutions to their other depots to further reduce the exposure of operators to vibration. Where both solutions are used together, the total reduction in vibration exposure will be 60%.

The result

- The new saws produce a vibration magnitude 53% lower than the typical old saws and they can be introduced without any change to the work system.
- The new tool is designed to reduce internal wear of parts and so maintenance costs are reduced.

Case courtesy of Chep (UK) Limited
Birmingham depot

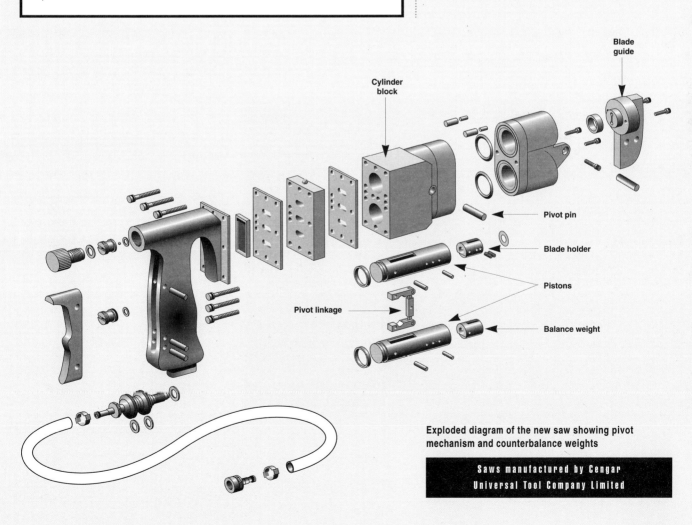

Exploded diagram of the new saw showing pivot mechanism and counterbalance weights

Saws manufactured by Cengar Universal Tool Company Limited

OUTDOOR POWER TOOLS PURCHASING POLICY

The task

Using chainsaws and strimmers.

The problem

The maintenance of watercourses often involves using chainsaws, strimmers and brushcutters to clear vegetation from river banks and similar areas. Local depots of a national organisation were free to purchase tools of their choice from local suppliers when required, which resulted in the company owning a large range of tools from a variety of manufacturers. A test session was held at which the vibration produced by a selection of the tools in use was measured under simulated work conditions. The chainsaws produced an average vibration magnitude of 13 m/s^2 with several tools reported to produce values above 25 m/s^2. The strimmers gave an average vibration magnitude of 8 m/s^2 with a significant number producing more than 15 m/s^2. It was very difficult to determine a representative vibration exposure time for the tools, however, discussion between tool operators and other staff revealed that daily exposures of more than 2 hours for a chainsaw and 4 hours for a strimmer were unlikely. This meant that personnel had potential exposures of 13 m/s^2 A(8) for chainsaws and 11 m/s^2 A(8) for strimmers.

Strimmer in use

The solution

A committee, including representatives of management, the unions and the operators, reviewed the existing situation and discussed the most appropriate measures to reduce vibration exposure. The objective was to reduce it to 2.8 m/s^2 A(8), which, using the estimated exposure times, could allow chainsaws to produce a maximum vibration magnitude of 5.6 m/s^2 and strimmers a maximum of 4 m/s^2. There was a lengthy period of consultation with tool suppliers, tool users and others to ensure that a sufficient range of tools meeting these criteria would be available and that all of the organisation's needs and obligations could be met. A purchasing policy was then prepared, under which all of the chainsaws and strimmers in stock would be replaced with tools which met the criteria within 4 years. The changes will be phased in with tools producing vibration magnitudes of more than 20 m/s^2 being withdrawn from use immediately, all tools producing more than 12.5 m/s^2 within 1 year, and the ultimate objective achieved within 4 years.

The cost

Minimal as tools would be replaced at the end of their life anyway.

The result

- A general reduction in vibration magnitudes produced by the tools used.
- The newer tools are often better designed and less noisy.
- The operators of the tools were involved in the development of the policy which helped to increase their awareness of the problem.

	Tool	Vibration magnitude $a_{h,w}$ in m/s^2	Time before daily exposure exceeds 2.8 m/s^2 A(8)	Daily exposure time	Daily exposure (m/s^2 A(8))
Old	Chainsaw	26	6 minutes	2 hours	13
	Strimmer	15	17 minutes	4 hours	11
New	Chainsaw	5.6 maximum	2 hours	2 hours	2.8
	Strimmer	4 maximum	4 hours	4 hours	2.8

LOW-VIBRATION FASTENER SYSTEM

The task

Assembling lightweight structures.

The problem

Aircraft wings produced at one factory were assembled using nuts and bolts. With this method, to ensure the integrity of the joint, the bolts are slightly larger than the holes drilled in the wing to take them and have to be forced into place with a riveting gun. In a simulated working cycle, a riveting gun produced an average vibration magnitude of 9.5 m/s^2. A worker might be exposed to this level for up to 1 hour a day with a similar period spent using a nutrunner (vibration magnitude of approximately 3 m/s^2) and the rest of the day drilling (vibration magnitude of less than 1 m/s^2).

The solution

The wings are now assembled using a pin/collar fastener system. This system uses swaged metal collars to secure pins (bolts) with simple parallel grooves rather than spiral threads. The pins are still slightly larger than the holes in the wing but are pulled into place with a special pneumatic tool rather than pushed through with a riveting gun. A metal ring or collar is then placed over each pin and a second special tool simultaneously pulls on the tail of the pin and pushes a conical die over the collar. This action clamps the joint together and locks it by deforming (swaging) the collar into the pin grooves. The tail of the pin then snaps off, leaving it flush with the newly swaged collar. The only source of vibration in this process, other than drilling the holes, is the shock produced by the pin tail breaking. This results in an average vibration magnitude of 1.5 m/s^2 over a typical working cycle. Each operator spends between 1 and 2 hours a day fitting the fasteners and the rest of the time drilling holes.

The cost

The fasteners are similar in cost to the nuts and bolts previously used. Tools cost about £1000 each.

The result

- There is a reduction in both the vibration magnitude produced and the time the operators are exposed.
- The noise levels are greatly reduced.
- The cycle is faster overall which increases productivity.
- The quality of work has improved because the clamping force is higher and more consistent and the finished joint is more resistant to loosening from vibration.

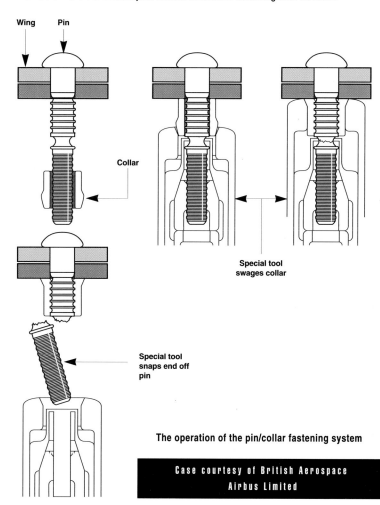

The operation of the pin/collar fastening system

Case courtesy of British Aerospace Airbus Limited

	Tools used	Vibration magnitude $a_{h,w}$ in m/s^2	Time before daily exposure exceeds 2.8 m/s^2 A(8)	Daily exposure time	Daily exposure (m/s^2 A(8))
Before	Riveting gun	9.5	42 minutes	1 hour	
	Nutrunner	3	7 hours	1 hour	Total of 3.6
	Drill	Less than 1	More than 24 hours	6 hours	
After	Pin/collar tools	1.5	More than 24 hours	1 hour 30 minutes	Total of 1.1
	Drill	Less than 1	More than 24 hours	6 hours 30 minutes	

30 NO CONTACT CASTING SHELL KNOCKOUT

The task

Knocking out multiple-component ceramic moulds used in the 'lost wax' casting process.

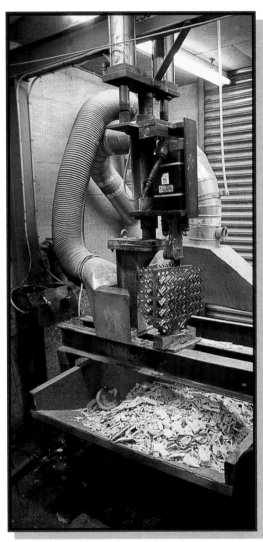

Knockout machine showing breaker mounted in support frame

The problem

A precision casting company used a hand-held riveting hammer, of a type used in shipyards, to knock out castings from the ceramic shells in which they had been cast. This process takes approximately 20 minutes to complete per multiple component mould, exposing the operator to vibration magnitudes of up to 12 m/s^2. Typically an operator would knock out 18 such moulds a day giving a possible exposure of 10 m/s^2 A(8).

The solution

The company developed an in-house solution by mounting a pneumatic breaker, similar to the type used to dig up the road, in a custom-built steel support frame. The mould to be knocked out is held in the frame with pneumatic jaws and vibrated by a special toolpiece fitted in the breaker.

The cost

Approximately £2500 for the breaker, steel work and pneumatics plus engineer's time.

The result

- The operator does not come into contact with any vibrating parts.
- The time to knock out one mould tree reduced from 20 minutes to 5 minutes.
- There is a reduced risk of back problems as less lifting is required.
- The machine can be partially or fully enclosed to reduce the operator's exposure to noise.

	Vibration magnitude $a_{h,w}$ in m/s^2	Time before daily exposure exceeds 2.8 m/s^2 A(8)	Daily exposure time	Daily exposure (m/s^2 A(8))
Before	12	25 minutes	6 hours	10
After	0	–	0	–

LOW-VIBRATION RIVETERS AND REACTION BARS

31

The task

Riveting aeroplane wings.

The problem

Aircraft wings are often assembled using rivets. A hole is drilled through the components to be joined and a rivet inserted. The joint is then made by flaring the point of the rivet with an impulsive tool (riveting gun) while the other end is supported with a reaction bar. In a typical operation at one factory the wing components were held in a jig while the riveting was done by two workers. One worker operated the riveting gun and the other held the reaction bar, a solid block of metal, in place. A full day's riveting requires about 2 hours use of the tools, giving vibration exposures of about 2 m/s² A(8) and 9 m/s² A(8) for riveting and reacting respectively.

The solution

The company invested in new tools with the specific intention of reducing hand-arm vibration exposure. They bought vibration-reduced riveting guns and vibration-isolated reaction bars which have reduced the vibration magnitude experienced by both operators to 3 m/s². The gun has an improved internal design and the reaction bar features a passive spring/damper system to reduce the vibration.

The cost

Low-vibration riveters cost about twice the price of normal ones. Vibration-damped reaction bars cost about £300.

The result

■ Vibration magnitude has reduced for both the riveting and reacting operations.
■ The new tools are more comfortable for the operators to use.

Case courtesy of British Aerospace Airbus Limited

Low-vibration tools being used to rivet an aircraft wing

	Operation	Vibration magnitude $a_{h,w}$ in m/s²	Time before daily exposure exceeds 2.8 m/s² A(8)	Daily exposure time	Daily exposure (m/s² A(8))
Before	Riveting	5	2 hours 30 minutes	2 hours	2.5
	Reacting	17	13 minutes	2 hours	8.5
After	Riveting	3	7 hours	2 hours	1.5
	Reacting	3	7 hours	2 hours	1.5

SPECIAL FORMWORK AVOIDS SCABBLING

The task

Construction of large concrete structures.

The problem

A construction company was awarded a contract to build one of the stations for the London Underground Jubilee Line Extension. The station design included a reinforced concrete base slab 300 m long, 25 m wide and 3 m deep. The slab was cast *in situ* in 43 sections, each 7 m long. The sections were cast one after another using the previous section to support one side and a specially constructed formwork stop end to support the other. With this method of construction it is important that the new concrete makes an effective bond with the old. When wooden formwork is used, this bond can only be achieved by removing the top surface of the concrete to reveal the aggregate underneath. This is often done with impulsive tools in a process known as scabbling. In this case, the tools were used for about 2 hours per day and exposed operators to high vibration magnitudes (typically 15 m/s^2). At that work rate, each stop end would have taken approximately eight worker shifts to scabble with a vibration exposure of about 8 m/s^2 A(8).

The solution

The company used an expanded metal material to construct the formwork for the stop end mating surfaces. The material was ribbed and featured bent tabs of mesh which, when concrete was poured behind it, become embedded in the concrete, forming a bond. The formwork was left in place once the concrete had cured and when the next section was poured, it formed a bond with the outer surface of the expanded metal that was as strong as a traditional scabbled joint. No scabbling was necessary.

The cost

The expanded metal formwork cost approximately £7 per m^2.

The result

- The operators were not exposed to any vibration.
- It was installed more quickly than using wooden formwork as it allowed the next section of concrete to be poured before the previous section was fully cured (set).
- Noise and dust levels were also reduced.

Scraping away excess material during pouring

Case courtesy of Tarmac Bachy Joint Venture

Example of *in situ* cast concrete showing expanded metal formwork

	Vibration magnitude $a_{h,w}$ in m/s^2	Time before daily exposure exceeds 2.8 m/s^2 A(8)	Daily exposure time	Daily exposure (m/s^2 A(8))
Before (estimated)	15	17 minutes	2 hours	7.5
After	0	–	0	–

PAINT-ON MATERIAL AVOIDS SCABBLING

The task

Preparing cast concrete for adhesion to new material.

The problem

Large concrete structures are generally cast in stages by pouring liquid concrete into fabricated moulds. To ensure correct adhesion between stages it is necessary to roughen, or scabble, the mating surfaces of the hardened concrete. On one site, needle guns that exposed operators to vibration magnitudes of 9 m/s^2 were sometimes used for this operation for nearly 2 hours per day.

The solution

The company used a retarder. This is a material which can be painted onto the inside of the mould in the areas where scabbling would have been necessary. This prevents the surface concrete from curing so that the top few millimetres of material can be removed with a standard pressure washer after removal of the mould, leaving a surface ideal for adhesion. The material can be used safely by following the handling instructions on the safety data sheets supplied by the manufacturer.

The cost

Approximately £180 for a drum of retarder with a coverage of about 100 m^2.

The result

■ There is no vibration exposure for the operators.

■ It increases productivity, eg a job which would have taken half a day with needle guns can now be done in 10 minutes with reduced cost.

■ Noise and dust exposure are reduced.

Removing excess material with jet washer

	Vibration magnitude $a_{h,w}$ in m/s^2	Time before daily exposure exceeds 2.8 m/s^2 A(8)	Daily exposure time	Daily exposure (m/s^2 A(8))
Before	9	46 minutes	2 hours	4
After	0	–	0	–

The task

Constructing concrete structures.

The problem

A construction company was building one of the stations for the London Underground Jubilee Line extension. The main structure of the station is concrete which was being cast *in situ* in stages. The meeting surfaces of each section have to be prepared before the adjacent section is cast to ensure an effective bond. In some parts of the structure, this was done using a special expanded metal material which forms the bond itself (see also Case Study 32). However, this material is not suitable for use on thin sections of concrete which meant the joints in these sections had to be prepared in some other way. They could have been prepared using impulsive scabbling tools such as needle guns, but workers would have been exposed to vibration magnitudes of 15 m/s^2 for up to 2 hours per shift. These tools also produce high noise levels.

The solution

The surfaces were prepared by grit blasting. A sub-contract gang was able to blast about 300 m^2 of the surfaces per day per worker. Before the work began, screens were erected around the area to be blasted to prevent dust from blowing around the site. The grit blasting method compares favourably with the use of impulsive scabblers which may prepare as little as 8 m^2 of the surface per day per worker.

The cost

Sub-contracted grit blasting on this project cost about £3 per m^2.

The result

- The operators are not exposed to any vibration with grit blasting.
- Grit blasting is much faster than scabbling but may increase exposure to dust and noise which will require further assessment and control measures.

Case courtesy of Tarmac Bachy Joint Venture

	Vibration magnitude $a_{h,w}$ in m/s^2	Time before daily exposure exceeds 2.8 m/s^2 A(8)	Daily exposure time	Daily exposure (m/s^2 A(8))
Before (typical)	15	17 minutes	2 hours	7.5
After	0	–	0	–

REDUCED-VIBRATION POLE SCABBLER

The task

Making large, *in situ* cast concrete structures.

The problem

A construction company needed to make many large concrete components at the site of a large bridge building project. The components were cast in stages. A batch of concrete is poured into a mould and allowed to harden before the next batch is poured on. To ensure that the successive stages bond together effectively, the surface of each is roughed or 'scabbled' once it has hardened. On flat horizontal surfaces this can be done with a pole scabbler, a reciprocating tool fitted with a sharp point which breaks up the concrete. The vibration produced by these tools can be very high, for example a magnitude of 40 m/s^2 was measured on one old tool used at the bridge site. This particular tool is rarely used now, but an average daily usage of 1 hour would give an exposure of 14 m/s^2 A(8).

The solution

Pole scabblers which include vibration reducing features are now available. One such tool was used at the bridge site and produced a vibration magnitude of 7.5 m/s^2. With 1 hour's use a day this would give an exposure of less than 3 m/s^2 A(8). The tool features spring/damper systems to absorb the vibration produced by the impact of the point. This makes the tool heavier than the old type but the effects of this have been reduced by fitting a handle to the shaft which improves control.

The cost

The reduced-vibration pole scabbler used in this case costs about 50% more than an equivalent normal type.

The result

- The vibration magnitude produced by the new tools is reduced.
- The operators say they prefer using the new tools.
- The new tool is fitted with a handle on the shaft which improves control, particularly on flat surfaces.

New reduced-vibration pole scabbler

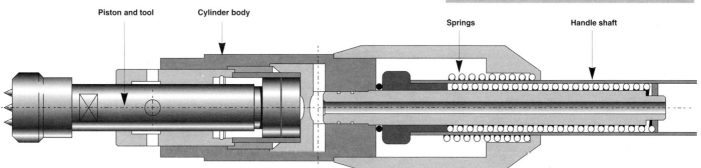

Cross-section of vibration-reducing features of tool, showing isolating springs

	Vibration magnitude $a_{h,w}$ in m/s^2	Time before daily exposure exceeds 2.8 m/s^2 A(8)	Daily exposure time	Daily exposure (m/s^2 A(8))
Before (typical)	40	2 minutes	1 hour	14
After	7.5	1 hour 5 minutes	1 hour	2.6

36 DEBURRING WITH RUMBLER

The task

Removing sharp edges from small pressed components.

The problem

At one factory small pressed components were deburred using emery bands mounted on rubber cylinders fitted to straight grinders. The component is held in one hand and the tool in the other so both hands are exposed to vibration. The magnitude of the vibration exposure varies depending on the size and type of component. A typical average vibration magnitude would be 2 m/s^2 and exposure could be as long as 7 hours, with each component taking about 2 minutes to complete.

The solution

The components are now deburred by rumbling. This process involves placing a batch of components in a container along with a large quantity of small pieces of abrasive material. The container is then vibrated vigorously (rumbled) which causes the components and abrasive pieces to rub against each other, removing the burrs. A batch of about 500 components takes 20 minutes to deburr in the machine.

The cost

Deburring machines cost approximately £5000 each. Abrasive material costs are reduced significantly.

The result

- The operators are not exposed to any vibration.
- There has also been a significant increase in productivity.
- Rumbling machines may produce high noise levels from which operators must be protected.

The rumbling machine now used to deburr small components

	Vibration magnitude $a_{h,w}$ in m/s^2	Time before daily exposure exceeds 2.8 m/s^2 A(8)	Daily exposure time	Daily exposure (m/s^2 A(8))
Before	2	16 hours	7 hours	1.9
After	0	–	0	–

The task

Fettling and preparing metal fabrications.

The problem

At a large-scale precision engineering factory, small fabrications are fettled using a range of tools. The majority of the tools used are straight grinders of different sizes fitted with a variety of toolpieces. One tool, fitted with a rotary burr, produced an average vibration magnitude of 2 m/s^2 over a typical working cycle. The actual exposure time for each tool varies from day to day.

The solution

The company recently started using hand-held belt grinders which typically produce vibration magnitudes of around 0.5 m/s^2. These tools can be used for most of the jobs previously done with straight grinders, giving a significant reduction in vibration exposure and several other advantages.

The cost

Belt grinders are available in several sizes and cost about £700 compared with £100 to £200 for equivalent straight grinders. Overall, the cost of abrasive belts is similar to other types of tool. The belts are available in a range of widths, lengths and abrasive grades.

The result

- The vibration magnitude produced has reduced.
- The tools are easier to control and less prone to wander and kick.
- The belts can be changed very quickly.
- The operator needs to apply less force to operate the belt grinder.
- Access to awkward areas is much improved.

Rotary file being used to fettle a component

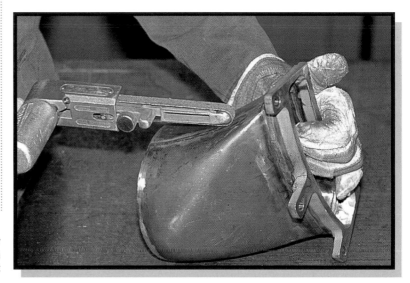

Hand-held belt grinder being used to fettle a component

	Vibration magnitude $a_{h,w}$ in m/s^2	Time before daily exposure exceeds 2.8 m/s^2 A(8)	Daily exposure time	Daily exposure (m/s^2 A(8))
Before	2	16 hours	Varies	Varies
After	0.5	More than 24 hours	Varies	Varies

GROUP WORKING WITH SUSPENDED TOOLS

The task

General assembly tasks in a car engine plant.

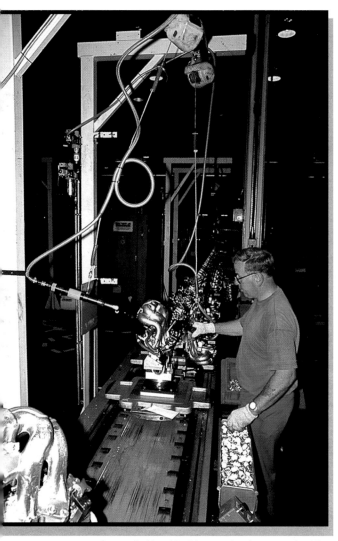

Suspended hand tool in use, showing support cable

The problem

Engine assembly involves many different tasks. A long time is spent sorting, checking and aligning components and putting together sub-assemblies. There are also many threaded connections which have to be started, run-up and tightened to a specified torque. These tasks are done by one person using pneumatic hand tools that produce vibration magnitudes as high as 8 m/s^2. Although the tools are not in constant use, they are used for about an hour per day, and daily vibration exposures are likely to reach the HSE recommended action level of 2.8 m/s^2 A(8). These tools are heavy which may put a strain on the wrist, worsening some of the effects of hand-arm vibration syndrome.

The solution

On one new engine assembly line a work group system is used. This involves a group of four or five people per shift sharing various assembly tasks. In the general assembly area, this halves the time for which any individual is exposed to vibration in a day. Nut running and torquing up is done with low stall-torque clutch-operated tools (ie the tool keeps turning the nut until it reaches a pre-set torque) which produces vibration magnitudes of approximately 2.5 m/s^2. These tools and others are suspended from overhead counterbalance systems, which takes their weight and holds them at an appropriate height for the required task.

The cost

Tools cost £1000 each. The suspension mechanism costs about £1500.

The result

- ■ A reduction in vibration magnitude is produced.
- ■ The risk of wrist strain is reduced.
- ■ Ergonomics are improved as suspended tools come easily to hand.
- ■ Operators report that group working reduces boredom and fatigue.

Case courtesy of Ford Motor Company

	Vibration magnitude $a_{h,w}$ in m/s^2	Time before daily exposure exceeds 2.8 m/s^2 A(8)	Daily exposure time	Daily exposure (m/s^2 A(8))
Before (potential)	8	1 hour	1 hour	2.8
After (typical)	2.5	10 hours	30 minutes	Less than 1

INSTALLATION OF HYDRAULIC CROPPING MACHINE

The task

Removing flash and excess metal (fettling) from nodular iron castings.

The problem

At one foundry, cast exhaust manifolds used to be fettled by two groups of five workers using hand tools. In this process, one worker knocks off the larger pieces with a lump hammer and then puts the castings onto a conveyor. The casting is carried to three others who in turn operate a large pedestal grinder, a chipping hammer and a straight grinder. Finally a fifth person inspects the castings for any defects. The chipper and straight grinder used are types which can produce vibration magnitudes as high as 12 m/s^2 and 6 m/s^2 respectively. The pedestal grinder is of the type which can expose operators to magnitudes of around 10 m/s^2. Lump hammer operations of this type produce a typical magnitude of 27 m/s^2. Observation showed that each operation resulted in vibration exposure for about 15% of the time, and as the group rotated between the five jobs, the total exposure for each group member could have been nearly 6 m/s^2 A(8).

The solution

The company installed a hydraulic cropping machine, in which the castings are held in a fixture and the bulk of the flash is removed with a single blow from a specially made tool, pushed by a hydraulic press. Some work still has to be done with the grinders, although much less than before. The lump hammer is no longer used at all. With the new machine, a single, rotating group of six people fettle marginally more castings in a day than the two old groups together. Vibration exposure is about 1.7 m/s^2 A(8).

The cost

£600 000 for the cropping machine, including £100 000 for tooling.

The result

- Daily vibration exposure for the operators has reduced.
- The machine has improved quality, and produces a more consistent and neat finish.
- Productivity has improved by about 80%.

Casting before fettling

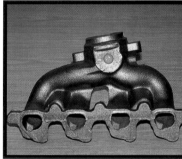

Casting after fettling

Cropping machine showing castings in fixtures

	Operation	Vibration magnitude $a_{h,w}$ in m/s^2	Time before daily exposure exceeds 2.8 m/s^2 A(8)	Daily exposure time	Daily exposure (m/s^2 A(8))
Before (with	Pedestal grinder	10	38 minutes	15 minutes	
typical tools)	Straight grinder	6	2 hours 30 minutes	15 minutes	5.8
	Lump hammer	27	5 minutes	15 minutes	
After (with	Pedestal grinder	10	38 minutes	5 minutes	1.2
typical tools)	Straight grinder	6	2 hours 30 minutes	5 minutes	

The task

Quarrying for masonry stone.

Rock drilling in progress

Excavator at work in a quarry

The problem

Masonry stone can often be quarried without the use of explosives. Blocks of stone are loosened from the ground with hand-held tools and lifted away with mobile cranes. Only large blocks of regular shape and colour are of use. Irregular and small blocks are broken up with pneumatic breakers and removed by hand. Good blocks are squared up by rock drilling rows of holes and splitting the stone by hammering wedges into the holes. Pneumatic breakers and rock drills produce typical vibration magnitudes of 12 m/s^2 and 15 m/s^2 respectively. Also sledgehammers are used which expose the operator to shock vibration with a typical magnitude of around 25 m/s^2. In one small limestone quarry, it is estimated that approximately 1.25 hours was spent rock drilling, 1.5 hours breaking, and 8 minutes hammering in an average day, giving a typical daily exposure of nearly 9 m/s^2 A(8).

The solution

A large 360° tracked excavator is used to pull blocks of stone from the quarry face and break up the unwanted material. Blocks are extracted by scraping out and enlarging natural fissures in the rock around the block and levering them out. Good blocks are then finished with the rock drills as before. Unwanted material is removed by the excavator so no pneumatic breaking is necessary. There is a small reduction in the use of rock drills and sledgehammers giving a typical daily exposure of 6.1 m/s^2 A(8). The next step for the company is to buy modern, low-vibration rock drills when the existing units need replacement.

The cost

The excavator is leased for £800 per week including the driver.

The result

■ No pneumatic breaking is necessary which reduces the time the operator is exposed to vibration.

■ Dust and noise exposure is reduced as workers are not close to the breaking rocks.

■ Productivity has improved.

Case courtesy of Rattee and Kett Limited

	Operation	Vibration magnitude $a_{h,w}$ in m/s^2	Time before daily exposure exceeds 2.8 m/s^2 A(8)	Daily exposure time	Daily exposure (m/s^2 A(8))
Before	Rock drilling	15	17 minutes	1 hour 15 minutes	
	Breaking	12	26 minutes	1 hour 30 minutes	8.6
	Hammering	25	6 minutes	8 minutes	
After	Rock drilling	15	17 minutes	1 hour	6.1
	Hammering	25	6 minutes	7 minutes	

TOOL STOCK AUDIT AND PURCHASING POLICY

The task

Preparation and dressing of metal fabrications and castings.

The problem

A large shipyard in Northern England had more than 400 straight grinders of various sizes in stock. The tools were used all over the yard and their daily usage varied greatly. It is possible that during a full day an operator could use a range of similar tools. The highest vibration magnitude measured on a straight grinder at the site was about 7 m/s^2.

The solution

The company decided to measure the vibration magnitude produced by every tool in stock. To do this they bought a vibration meter and transducer set and trained staff members to use them. This exercise produced results in the range 1 to 7 m/s^2. The tools producing the highest vibration were quarantined immediately and where possible, the use of the low-vibration tools was encouraged. Alongside this programme, the company made vibration performance a condition of purchase for new tooling. It was decided that by only buying grinders that produced vibration magnitudes lower than 2.8 m/s^2, vibration exposure should be kept at a reasonable level regardless of exposure time. The decision to buy a tool is based both on manufacturer's claimed data and tests performed at the yard. The vibration performance of the tools will be monitored at intervals to check for deterioration.

The cost

Quality hand-arm vibration measurement equipment starts at around £3000. Alternatively, instrumentation can be hired. Staff can be trained to use the equipment in one day and assistance may be provided by the instrument vendor.

The result

- The vibration magnitude produced has reduced by 60 %.
- The measurement equipment can also be used to monitor vibration in other parts of the yard.
- The process has improved control of the existing stock of tools.

	Vibration magnitude $a_{h,w}$ in m/s^2	Time before daily exposure exceeds 2.8 m/s^2 A(8)	Daily exposure time	Daily exposure (m/s^2 A(8))
Before (potential)	7	1 hour 15 minutes	Varies	Varies
After	2.8	8 hours	Varies	Varies

42 HANDS-FREE LINISHING

The task

Using linishers (abrasive belt grinders) to remove excess material from castings (fettling).

The problem

In the foundry industry, many pedestal-mounted linishers are used. On these linishers, the operator holds the components to be fettled and pushes them against the abrasive belt. Although the vibration experienced by the operator varies depending on the type of component and the pressure applied, vibration magnitudes of about 8 m/s^2 are typical. It is unlikely that an operator working at the machine for a full shift would be exposed to the vibration for more than 2 hours, giving a possible exposure of 4 m/s^2 A(8).

Hand-held linishing machine

The solution

At one foundry the manual linishers were replaced with automatic ones. The component is held in a specially made jig and pushed onto the belt by pneumatic rams.

The cost

Each new grinder costs between £20 000 and £30 000. The mounting fixture to hold the casting in place was made in-house by maintenance staff from mild steel.

The result

- The operator does not come into contact with any vibrating parts.
- The cycle time for each component has been cut from about 5 minutes to 30 seconds, and produces a more consistent finish.
- Noise exposure and the potential risk of injury due to contact with the belt has reduced.

Automatic linishing machine

	Vibration magnitude $a_{h,w}$ in m/s^2	Time before daily exposure exceeds 2.8m/s^2 A(8)	Daily exposure time	Daily exposure (m/s^2 A(8))
Before	8	1 hour	2 hours	4
After	0	–	0	–

BELT GRINDING AND POLISHING OF CERAMIC WARE

The task

Polishing out blemishes on ceramic ware.

The problem

The traditional method for rectifying blemishes on ceramic ware is to polish the ware using pedestal grinders fitted with polishing stones. In use, these stones quickly wear to an irregular shape, resulting in high vibration. The operators are highly skilled and work very fast, polishing up to 100 pieces per hour for 7 hours a day. During a simulated working cycle, an average vibration magnitude of 4 m/s^2 was measured on a plate being polished on one such machine.

The solution

The pedestal grinders were replaced with specially designed bench-top belt grinding and polishing machines (linishers). These require less skill to operate and are much faster (up to 250 pieces per hour) with a typical work cycle average vibration magnitude of 2 m/s^2.

The cost

£2500 for a bench-top linisher. The polishing material costs per piece are similar to the traditional method.

The result

- The vibration magnitude produced has halved.
- The new machines produce a more consistent finish and give more control to the operator.
- They produce less noise.
- They can be used on a wider range of materials and are much preferred by the operators.

Ware being polished with a pedestal machine

Ware being polished with a bench-top linisher machine

Case courtesy of Spode Limited
Bench-top linishers are available from SECO Engineering Company Limited

	Vibration magnitude $a_{h,w}$ in m/s^2	Time before daily exposure exceeds 2.8 m/s^2 A(8)	Daily exposure time	Daily exposure (m/s^2 A(8))
Before	4	4 hours	7 hours	3.7
After	2	16 hours	7 hours	1.8

44 ISOLATION FOR GRINDING OPERATION

The task

Fettling cast components with a pedestal grinder.

The problem

A foundry used a large pedestal grinder to remove flash and other unwanted material from aluminium castings. In this process, an operator holds the casting in both hands and supports it in a fixture while pushing it, with some force, against the grinding wheel. The fixture was supported by a flimsy fabricated bracket mounted on the body of the grinder. Mechanical vibrations, due to out-of-balance forces in the machine, caused the bracket to resonate which in turn caused the fixture and the casting to vibrate. This transmitted very high vibration magnitudes to the operator's hands. The operator could be in contact with the vibration for up to 4 hours per day and a daily vibration exposure greater than 14 m/s^2 A(8) was possible.

The solution

A firm of consultants was employed to investigate the cause of the vibration and find a solution. The casting fixture support bracket was identified as the principal cause of the problem. A replacement was designed with a more rigid construction to be mounted directly on the floor rather than on the machine. The new bracket was made and fitted by the company's own engineering staff.

The cost

£20 for materials. Approximately half a day's labour plus consultant's time.

The result

■ The vibration experienced by the operator has reduced to less than a tenth of the original.

■ Improved control of the component has resulted in a more consistent finish.

Casting fixture support methods showing how the operator was isolated from the vibration

BEFORE

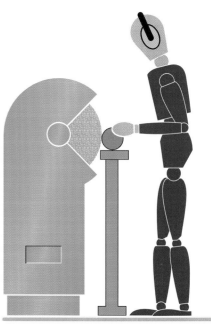

AFTER

	Vibration magnitude $a_{h,w}$ in m/s^2	Time before daily exposure exceeds 2.8 m/s^2 A(8)	Daily exposure time	Daily exposure (m/s^2 A(8))
Original support	More than 20	Less than 9 minutes	4 hours	More than 14
New support	1.5	More than 24 hours	4 hours	1

LASER CUTTER REPLACES NIBBLING MACHINE

The task

Cutting shapes from thick metal sheets.

The problem

At one large-scale precision engineering factory, sheet metal used to be cut to shape using a nibbling machine. This is a large punch press fitted with a small tool which pierces the metal approximately ten times per second. The cut is made by guiding the sheet by hand so that the tool slowly 'nibbles' a slot at approximately 10 mm per second. The average vibration magnitude, measured at the point where the hand was holding one sheet of 3 mm steel, was 9 m/s^2. The company had four such machines in use, when necessary, operated by a large pool of workers who spent the remainder of their time performing other general fabrication duties. The machine could not cut to precise dimensions, leaving a rough edge on the sheet, so that grinding was necessary to bring the components to the correct size and finish. A typical day might have included 2 hours' grinding (with tools producing vibration magnitudes of 2 m/s^2) and 1 hour on the nibbling machine. This would give a total typical daily vibration exposure of over 3 m/s^2 A(8).

Nibbling machine

The solution

The company invested in a flat-bed carbon-dioxide laser cutter which, with one trained operator, does the work previously done by the four nibbling machines. The machine is computer controlled and there is no contact with vibrating surfaces. It also cuts more accurately than the nibbler so no grinding is necessary. The other staff now concentrate on other duties with no exposure to vibration.

The cost

About £400 000 to buy the laser cutter plus £20 000 per year for tooling and gases. The punch presses would cost about £50 000 each. In other situations a smaller laser cutting machine, or one using plasma or flame cutting, could be used, which could be much cheaper.

The result

- The operators are not exposed to any vibration.
- The laser is very efficient with fast and more accurate cutting.
- It can cut much larger sheets.
- It has removed the risk of injuring hands in the punch press and has reduced noise exposure.

Laser cutting

	Operation	Vibration magnitude $a_{h,w}$ in m/s^2	Time before daily exposure exceeds 2.8 m/s^2 A(8)	Daily exposure time	Daily exposure (m/s^2 A(8))
Before (typical)	Nibbler	9	46 minutes	1 hour	3.3
	Grinding	2	16 hours	2 hours	
After	–	0	–	0	–

MAINTAINING BLOOD CIRCULATION CASE STUDIES

The primary cause of HAVS is work which involves holding vibrating tools or workpieces. The risk depends on both the vibration magnitude and how long people are exposed to it. Several other factors also affect the severity of the risk, although there is still only limited scientific information on their importance and the way they interact. These include factors affecting blood circulation, such as temperature and smoking, which may be particularly important in the development of vibration white finger (VWF).

Although the main aim is to reduce the exposure of workers to hand-arm vibration, there are other activities which can help to improve working conditions. Keeping the body and hands warm helps to maintain a good blood flow to the fingers and may reduce the risk of injury. Where people have to work in cold areas, specific measures might include wearing warm weatherproof clothing; using tools with heated handles; wearing gloves; and making arrangements to allow workers to warm their hands and bodies before starting work. Gloves are useful both for keeping hands warm and providing physical protection.

Encouraging employees to have an adequate regular food intake, and the availability of hot drinks in cold wet weather will help to maintain body temperature and blood circulation to the extremities. Massaging and exercising fingers during work breaks will also help the blood circulation. Avoiding or cutting down smoking should be encouraged.

GLOVES TO WARM HANDS

The task

Continuous drilling of large holes in heavy-gauge steel.

The problem

In one shipyard holes are drilled through thick metal structures in non-stop operations. The job is done with large magnetically mounted, multivane pneumatic drills. Although the vibration exposure of the operators is not particularly high, perhaps a magnitude of 1.4 m/s^2 for a maximum of 7 hours, some of the operators showed symptoms of vibration white finger (one of the conditions that make up HAVS). Staff at the yard felt that this may be due to the chilling effect of the exhaust air from the drills. The drills ran constantly for very long periods, becoming encrusted with ice on damp days.

The solution

Operators were supplied with standard lattice-coated knitted gloves, chosen specifically to keep their hands warm. If cutting oil is used, they are used in combination with rubber gloves to prevent the potentially harmful oil coming into contact with the skin.

The cost

Approximately £1 a pair.

The result

■ Operators report greatly improved comfort.

Although this solution does not affect the actual measured vibration exposure, hand and body temperature do affect peripheral circulation and are believed to have an effect on the development of vibration white finger.

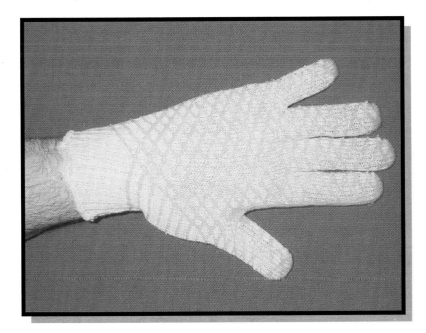

Glove of the type used to keep drill operators' hands warm

DUCT AWAY EXHAUST AIR

The task

Preparing, modifying or finishing metal components using pneumatic tools.

The problem

Concern about exposure to dust led a Midlands foundry to stop using pneumatic tools which were blowing exhaust air onto the workpiece. Unfortunately, alternative tools tend to exhaust the air in the direction of the operator's hands. The cooling effect of this air can cause discomfort and it is believed that cold hands may be more susceptible to the effects of vibration white finger (one of the conditions that make up HAVS), even if the vibration exposure remains the same.

The solution

To keep the exhaust air away from the operator's hands, an exhaust duct was made up from scrap tubing and old gauntlets and taped to the supply hose to discharge air away from the handles of the tool.

The cost

Scrap materials, a little tape and a few minutes of time.

The result

- Operators report improved comfort.
- The duct gives some protection to the connection between the tool and the air-line (the tool-hose union).
- Proprietary systems are available which incorporate silencers.

Although this solution does not affect the actual measured vibration exposure, hand and body temperature do affect peripheral circulation and are believed to have an effect on the development of vibration white finger.

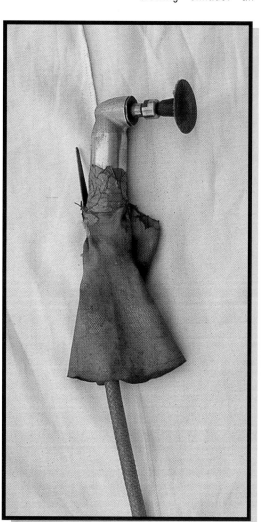

Small angle grinder fitted with an old gauntlet sleeve to duct exhaust air away from the operator's hands

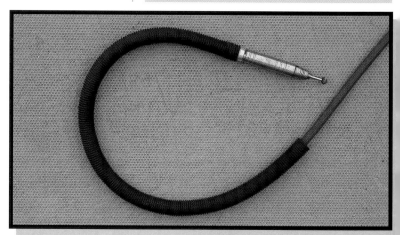

Small straight grinder fitted with a length of pipe to duct away exhaust air

HEATED HANDLES

Using chainsaws in forestry.

The problem

In commercial forestry, workers are often required to work outside all day in very cold conditions. The cold reduces the blood flow to the hands and fingers of the forestry workers which may increase the effects of vibration produced by tools such as chainsaws. As the work may be a long way from shelter, keeping the hands warm can be difficult.

The solution

Chainsaws are available with heating mechanisms in the handles. These generally feature electric heating elements which can be switched on and off. In combination with gloves, these handles can keep the hands warm all day if necessary.

The cost

Heated handles add approximately 10% to the cost of a professional chainsaw.

The result

■ Warm hands are more comfortable throughout the day.

Although this solution does not affect the actual measured vibration exposure, hand and body temperature do affect peripheral circulation and are believed to have an effect on the development of vibration white finger.

Typical chainsaw use

49

HOT AIR TO WARM HANDS

The task

Using grinders and linishers in a precision foundry.

The problem

At a large precision foundry, people working in the fettling area have to use various pieces of equipment which can expose them to potentially hazardous hand-arm vibration. Many of the operators walk or cycle to work and in winter they can often arrive with very cold hands. This results in circulation problems which could increase the risk of injury from vibration.

The solution

The company installed an ordinary warm-air hand dryer in the workshop locker area. The workers are able to use this to warm up their hands before starting to use the vibrating equipment.

The cost

Dryers cost about £150 and can be leased.

The result

■ Warm hands are more comfortable as well as less prone to vibration damage.

Although this solution does not affect the actual measured vibration exposure, hand and body temperature do affect peripheral circulation and are believed to have an effect on the development of vibration white finger.

Operator using hot air hand dryer to warm hands before beginning work

HEALTH SURVEILLANCE

Employers are required by law[2] to provide appropriate health surveillance for their employees taking account of risks identified in a risk assessment. The purpose of health surveillance is to detect adverse health effects at an early stage so that action can be taken to prevent further harm to employees. Health surveillance can also give you feedback on your risk assessment and the effectiveness of your control measures.

What effects on individuals there are likely to be from exposure to vibration cannot be known with any certainty, and HSE therefore recommends a programme of health surveillance for all employees who work regularly with vibrating tools or machines.

A good programme should include checking workers under the general supervision of a medical practitioner, preferably one who has training and experience in occupational medicine. Ideally the check should include a questionnaire and clinical examination and be undertaken initially at pre-employment and then on a regular basis, usually annually. Workers should be encouraged to report any HAVS symptoms, eg finger blanching (which should be investigated), to a designated person. Adequate records and documentation should be kept of routine health surveillance procedures and of any reported symptoms and their associated investigation.

The examples in this section illustrate some methods available for objective testing. HSE is currently undertaking work to investigate the standardisation of the tests and guidance will be published giving agreed methods for these tests.

More advice about health surveillance is contained in the HSE guidance book on hand-arm vibration (HS(G)88).[4]

HEALTH SURVEILLANCE ON A CONSTRUCTION SITE

The problem

Construction site workers are exposed to several potential sources of vibration. A wide variety of tools is used with unpredictable regularity, for varying lengths of time and often in cold or wet conditions. This, coupled with the fact that some people are more susceptible to the effects of HAVS than others, can make appropriate control of vibration exposure very difficult.

The solution

At one site, all workers potentially exposed to hazardous vibration are examined at regular intervals for signs of vibration white finger (VWF). Everyone is examined at least every 6 months, with anyone showing symptoms being seen more often. The company has compiled a list of the vibration magnitudes produced by all the tools on site from information supplied by the manufacturers. This information has been used to calculate an exposure time for each tool that would give a vibration exposure of 2.8 m/s^2 A(8). Programmes of preventive measures and health surveillance are recommended where workers' exposure regularly exceeds 2.8 m/s^2 A(8).

Workers showing no symptoms of HAVS are not restricted in the use of tools, but have been advised of the risks and as a result various formal and informal job rotation schemes exist to avoid high vibration exposures. People showing symptoms of VWF up to Stage One of the Stockholm Scale are restricted to exposure which is below 2.8 m/s^2 A(8), and kept on light duties for the rest of the time. Anyone exhibiting symptoms above Stage One of the Stockholm Scale is removed from all potential vibration exposure.

In this example, the examinations were carried out in the on-site medical centre. An alternative could be to use doctors specialising in occupational health on a consultancy basis.

Advice on the symptoms of HAVS, VWF and the Stockholm Scale is given in HSE's guidance *Hand-arm vibration*.[4]

SCREENING AND SURVEILLANCE METHODS IN AN AERO-ENGINE MANUFACTURER

This case study illustrates one company's approach to the use of different methods for objective testing.

The company introduced a surveillance system for their workers exposed to hand-arm vibration. This was organised by their medical department. The assessment consisted of six parts including a questionnaire. The works' doctor considered and reviewed the results of all the tests before any conclusions were drawn.

The six parts included the following:

1 Questionnaire

All the workers complete a questionnaire, similar to the one in HSE's *Hand-arm vibration*.[4] The range of questions includes hand symptoms, social history, leisure pursuits, vibration exposure and a report of the hand examination. The hand examination is done in the test room, which is kept at 24°C (plus or minus 2°C), so that the subject can acclimatise and the effect of the outside temperature can be removed. Acclimatisation generally takes about half an hour but in very cold weather may take longer.

2 Cold provocation test

The purpose of this technique is to demonstrate objectively an abnormal response of the finger to cold stimulation. The fingers of each hand are 'wired' up with thermocouples and placed (in a waterproof glove) in a tank of water at 15°C for 5 minutes. The rate at which the fingers rewarm after removal from the tank is logged by a computer to give a trace which can be interpreted. Early studies suggest that this test may have the potential to distinguish between VWF and primary Raynaud's phenomenon (also known as 'constitutional white finger' which is an inherited condition), as there are differences between the patterns of the finger rewarming traces produced by the two conditions. The test is not uncomfortable and is not designed to provoke an attack of VWF.

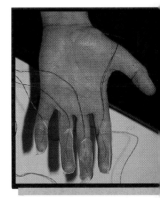

Hand fitted with thermocouples

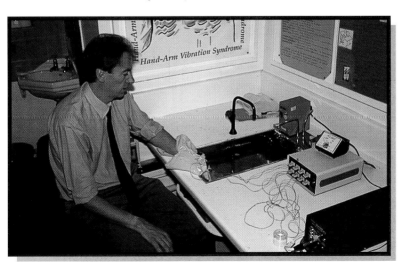

Hand in 15°C water tank for cold provocation test

3 Thermal aesthesiometry

Using a finger temperature pad, the subject's hot and cold temperature thresholds are determined by increasing or decreasing the temperature from a reference of 32.5°C. The subject reacts to a feeling of hot or cold by pressing a response button. The difference between the threshold of hot and cold temperatures is recorded as the Temperature Neutral Zone.

Thermal aesthesiometry test in progress

4 Grip strengths

The strength of grip for each hand is measured using a grip strength detector.

5 Vibrotactile threshold measurement

The threshold of sensitivity to vibration at 32.5 Hz and 125 Hz is measured using a counterbalanced vibration exciter. The subject's response is recorded by pushing a response button.

6 Gap detection aesthesiometry

The gap detection ability of fingers is tested by placing the finger on a tapering groove cut into a perspex block. The block is moved slowly to increase the gap until the subject can feel the groove. The minimum groove width that the subject can feel with the finger is recorded.

Gap detection aesthesiometry equipment

TABLE OF CASE STUDIES BY INDUSTRY

Industry	Study
Aerospace	29, 31, 51
Automotive	24, 25, 38,
Ceramics	43
Construction	4, 5, 6, 7, 20, 21, 32, 33, 34, 35, 50
Forestry	12, 48
Foundry	14, 16, 39, 44, 47, 49
Investment foundry	1, 17, 19, 30, 42
Pallet repair	26, 27
Power engineering	18
Precision engineering	2
Quarrying	40
Shipbuilding	3, 22, 23, 41, 46
Steel	15
Turbine manufacture	36, 37, 45
Utilities	8, 9, 10, 11
Watercourse maintenance	13, 28

TABLE OF CASE STUDIES BY REDUCTION METHOD

Method	Study
Change of machine	4, 8, 43
Change of process	5, 6, 7, 9, 18, 22, 23, 29, 32, 33, 34, 36, 39, 40, 45
Change of tool	37
Isolation	10, 15, 16, 19, 24, 30, 42, 44
Maintenance	12, 20
Management	13, 28, 38, 41
Process automation	1, 2, 17, 25, 26
Tool design	3, 11, 14, 21, 27, 31, 35
Maintaining blood circulation	46, 47, 48, 49
Health surveillance	50, 51

REFERENCES

1   *A guide to the Health and Safety at Work etc. Act 1974* (5th ed)
HSE Books 1992 ISBN 0 7176 0441 1

2   *Management of Health and Safety at Work Regulations 1992 Approved
Code of Practice* L21 HSE Books 1992 ISBN 0 7176 0412 8

3   *The Supply of Machinery (Safety) Regulations 1992*, as amended by the
Supply of Machinery (Safety) (Amendment) Regulations 1994 SI
1992/3073 HMSO 1992 ISBN 0 11 025719 7

4   *Hand-arm vibration* HS(G)88 HSE Books 1994 ISBN 0 7176 0743 7

5   *Selecting a health and safety consultancy* IND(G)133(L) HSE Books 1992
(free leaflet)

6   BS 6842:1987 *Guide to measurements and evaluation of human exposure
to vibration transmitted to the hand*

7   *Avoiding danger from underground services* HS(G)47 HSE Books 1989
ISBN 0 7176 0435 7

FURTHER READING

Surveillance of people exposed to health risks at work HS(G)61 HSE Books 1990 ISBN 0 7176 0525 6

Work equipment. Provision and Use of Work Equipment Regulations 1992 - Guidance on Regulations L22 HSE Books 1992 ISBN 0 7176 0414 4

HSE free leaflets

Hand-arm vibration: advice for employers IND(G)175(L) HSE Books 1994

Hand-arm vibration: advice on vibration white finger for employees and the self-employed IND(G)126(L) HSE Books 1994

Everyone's guide to RIDDOR 95 HSE 31 HSE Books 1996

Industry-specific guidance

Hazards associated with foundry processes: Rumbling - Noise hazards HSE Information Sheet. Foundries sheet no 7 (FNIS 7) HSE Books 1996

Hazards associated with foundry processes: Hand-arm vibration - The current picture HSE Information Sheet. Foundries sheet no 8 (FNIS 8) HSE Books 1996

Hazards associated with foundry processes: Hand-arm vibration - Symptoms and solutions HSE Information Sheet. Foundries sheet no 9 (FNIS 9) HSE Books 1996

Survey of exposure to hand-arm vibration in Great Britain: mines and quarries Research Paper 29 Bednall AW HSE Books 1991 ISBN 0 11 885900 5

Survey of exposure to hand-arm vibration in Great Britain: railway maintenance Research Paper 35 Bednall AW HSE Books 1994 ISBN 0 7176 0685 6

Reduction and control of noise and vibration in shipyards Shipbuilders and Ship-repairers Association (SSA) (May 1996) Available on subscription from: The Shipbuilders and Ship-repairer's Association, 33 Catherine Place, London SW1E 6DY Tel: 0171 828 0933 Fax: 0171 834 5747

Note: Many HSE leaflets are available free for single copies, but multiple orders may be supplied in priced packs.

For details of how to obtain HSE priced and free publications, see inside back cover.

British Standards are available from BSI Sales and Customer Services, 389 Chiswick High Road, London W4 4AL Tel: 0181 996 7000 Fax: 0181 996 7001.

The Stationery Office (formerly HMSO) publications are available from The Publications Centre, PO Box 276, London SW8 5DT. Tel: 0171 873 9090. They are also available from bookshops.

GLOSSARY

Angle grinder Rotary grinder in which the grinding wheel rotates at an angle to the motor axis. Can be fitted with grinding or cutting discs, shaped grinding stones and metal tools.

Anti-vibration mounts Soft mounts, usually a combination of rubber and metal, for vibrating machinery, designed to prevent vibration from the vibration source passing to the supporting structure. Also see 'Isolation'.

Balancer Tool suspension systems, using a counterbalance and pulleys, designed to prevent the operator having to lift the full weight of the tool.

Core drill Drill which cuts leaving a solid core which can be removed.

Curing The chemical process by which a material like cement becomes hard and strong.

Daily vibration exposure The combination of vibration magnitude with the period of exposure in a day, usually normalised to an 8-hour period and expressed as m/s^2 A(8). Daily vibration exposures can be compared with the HSE action level of 2.8 m/s^2 A(8), or the British Standard 6842: 1987, for guidance on risk or injury.

Damping Reducing vibration by attaching vibration-absorbing materials or devices.

Deburring Removing sharp edges from an object during manufacture.

Descaling Removing mill-scale (oxidised surface) from metal objects.

Declared (vibration) values The vibration value given by the tool manufacturer. This value is obtained from a standard test procedure. The value given by the manufacturer may not be the same as the vibration when the tool is being used. The declared vibration values are intended to allow comparison between similar tools from different manufacturers.

Dressing (of a grinding wheel) Removing the top surface of a grinding wheel to restore its shape and abrasive properties.

Fettling Removing unwanted material from a casting.

Fixture A specially made holder designed to fit a component perfectly and support it as the work is done.

Formwork Temporary structures used as moulds for concrete casting in building.

Frequency (Hz) A measure of the rate at which a vibrating surface moves back and forth. The frequency is measured in Hertz (Hz), equivalent to the number of cycles per second.

Isolation Reduction of vibration passing from one part of a machine (eg the motor) to another (eg the handles) using flexible connecting systems.

Investment casting Process for manufacturing metal objects by making a temporary mould around a replica made from a soft material such as wax by coating it in a ceramic material. As the ceramic material is fired, the wax flows away leaving a hollow mould into which the molten metal is poured.

Linisher A grinding machine which uses paper or fabric belts coated with abrasive material.

Pedestal grinder A grinding machine using a solid wheel of abrasive material mounted on a pedestal.

Resilient materials Soft, pliant materials which provide some vibration isolation.

Resonant frequency The frequency at which a structure will vibrate easily, producing relatively large vibrations from small input motions.

Root-mean-square (rms) Averaging method used for oscillating signals (the square-root of the arithmetic mean of a set of squared values).

Rotary burr A metal toolpiece fitted to a grinder.

Rotary file A straight grinder fitted with a metal toolpiece.

Rumbling Deburring small objects by shaking a large number of them together with abrasive material.

Runners and risers The waste parts of a casting where the molten metal flowed into the mould and between components.

Shot blasting (or direct pressure blasting) A surface preparation technique using small fragments of material such as slag or metal (shot) which are propelled by compressed air.

Straight grinder Rotary grinder in which the grinding wheel rotates in line with the axis of the motor. It can be fitted with grinding or cutting discs, shaped grinding stones and metal tools.

Stockholm Scale A classification system used to classify the vascular and neurological symptoms of HAVS.

Swaging Forming metal by application of pressure by a metal tool.

Tensioners A tool suspension system designed to prevent the operator having to lift the full weight of the tool.

Torque A measure of the tightness of a nut or bolt.

Vibration exposure See 'Daily vibration exposure'.

Vibration magnitude A measure of the average vibration level, using a root-mean-square average.

(Frequency) weighted vibration A measure of vibration magnitude which emphasises vibrations at the frequencies thought to be most damaging to the hand and arm.

ACKNOWLEDGEMENTS

The Health and Safety Executive acknowledges the generosity of the following companies who supplied information for cases or photographs/illustrations to help compile this publication:

ARM Utility Services Limited, Leyland

Atlas Copco Tools Limited, Hemel Hempstead

British Aerospace Airbus Limited, Chester

British Steel PLC, Swinden Technical Centre, Rotherham

Cengar Universal Tool Co. Limited, Halifax

Chep (UK) Limited, Birmingham Depot

Chep (UK) Limited, Bristol Depot

Compair Power Tools Limited, Swansea

Cornwall County Council, Redruth

European Gas Turbines, Industrial Products, Lincoln

Flexovit (UK) Limited, Congleton

Ford Motor Company, Bridgend

Forestry Commission, Dumfries

Hodge-Clemco Limited, Sheffield

Industrial Machine Tool Services Limited, Rochester

Industrial Noise and Vibration Centre, Slough

Mitsui Babcock Energy Services Limited, Tipton

National Rivers Authority, Almondsbury, Bristol

Outdoor Power Products Limited, Denton, Manchester

Rattee & Kett Limited, Cambridge

Rolls Royce Plc, Derby

SECO Engineering Co. Limited, Eversley

Specialist Services (Cutting and Drilling) Limited, Portsmouth

Spode Limited, Stoke-on-Trent

Svedala Limited, St Austell, Cornwall

Tarmac Bachy Joint Venture, London E14

Terrill Bros. (Founders) Limited, Hayle

Triplex Williams Limited, Cardiff

TT UK Limited, Bedford

Vickers Shipbuilding and Engineering Limited, Barrow-in-Furness